^{DR}
John Bastyr

PHILOSOPHY AND PRACTICE

DR
John Bastyr
PHILOSOPHY AND PRACTICE

Including
Bastyr's Clinical Homeopathic Materia Medica

BY
MELANIE J. GRIMES
RSHom (NA), CCH

ALETHEA BOOK COMPANY
SEATTLE • WASHINGTON

Published by
Alethea Book Company
Seattle, Washington

Copyright © 2005 by Melanie Grimes
Second printing 2014

ISBN: 0-9659550-4-4

Produced by CMYK Design Inc.

Printed by RR Donnelley in the United States of America

Dedicated to my sons, Julian, and Benjamin,
who taught me what health and vitality look like.

Contents

Introduction

Acknowledgements

History

1. Biography *15*
2. Bastyr and the History of Naturopathy *25*
3. Bastyr's Place in the History of Homeopathy *29*
4. History of Medicine and Homeopathy in Washington State *31*
5. Influences and Internships *34*

Philosophy

6. Philosophy *45*
7. Advice to Students *50*

Practice and Modalities

8. Homeopathy *55*
9. Hydrotherapy *77*
10. Botanical Medicine *81*
11. Electrotherapy *84*
12. Chiropractic *90*
13. Women's Health *91*
14. Pregnancy and Childbirth *94*
15. Treatment of Children *98*
16. Suggestions to Research *103*

Therapeutics

17. Clinical Homeopathic Materia Medica *107*
18. Treatment Guide *121*

Appendix

Photos *139*
Obituary *143*
Endnotes *145*

Introduction

Why this book?

I have to confess. I started out to be a naturopath and enrolled at NCNM in 1972. But after Dr. Bastyr loaned me his copy of Hahnemann's *Organon*, nothing has been the same. I became a homeopath.

I am also one of the women about whom Dr. B jokingly bragged, "I've gotten a lot of women pregnant." His homeopathic treatment enabled me to carry two beautiful sons to term, both now over 6 feet tall, tributes to some of his last pediatric cases. This book is written from the point of view of someone who was his patient for over 20 years, and who is an unabashed homeopath.

The book's focus is the practice and philosophy of Dr. Bastyr. However, (and this is where I express my unbridled enthusiasm for homeopathy) because of the importance of homeopathy as a modality in Bastyr's practice, and the fact that his work in other healing modalities has been covered elsewhere, I have extensively explored Dr B's work as a homeopath. Because, as Dr. B himself said, "I am a homeopath. I really believe in it fellows."

In the course of my research, I found that Bastyr was the rightful heir to an important position in the history of both naturopathy and homeopathy. Some of his important clinical findings were at risk of being lost for all time.

Most of the information in this book was gleaned from first or second party sources, from Bastyr or his students, directly from his lectures and lecture notes.

Bastyr was a link to the history of modern medicine, to the roots of the nature movement, as well as one of the earliest homeopaths in Washington State.

I hope his legacy will live on and inspire future generations.

Melanie Grimes
November, 2004

To past students:
If you find notebooks from Bastyr's classes, please let me know, as I hope to expand this work to include any additional materials.

Acknowledgments

I want to thank those who contributed material. First of all, the librarians at National College of Naturopathic Medicine. Without their generosity, this book would not have been possible. Julian Winston, and Sylvain Cazalet of Homéopathe International and *Simillimum*, Journal of HANP, for reprint of photos and text.

Also thanks to Dan Dixon, Bill Mitchell, Allen Moskowitz for sharing their memories. And to Andre Saine, and Andrew Lange.

Special thanks to the founders of Bastyr University, for keeping the name and memory of Dr. Bastyr alive: Joe Pizzorno, Bill Mitchell, Les Griffith.

Special thanks to those who led the homeopathic departments at naturopathic colleges over the years, including: Andrew Lange, Steve Olsen, Durr Elmore, John Collins, Ellen Goldman, Richard Mann, Will Taylor. Dr. B. would be proud.

To Karen Allen, the godmother of inspiration for book.

To Al Sampson for reading and advising.

To my mentors and healers.

To the makers of Microsoft Word software, who made the footnoting of this text a delight.

To my husband, Charles, for his continual support.

To my parents, Leo and Laura Kornfeld, for teaching me to love to learn.

To my children for teaching me to love to live.

HISTORY

1.
Biography

John Bastyr was a bridge

Bastyr was a bridge between the old eclectics, modern naturopathy, and the future of scientific research. His life bridged from roots in Europe to the start of a medical community in Seattle with links to Seattle's city fathers.

Bastyr believed in using "whatever it takes"[1] to treat a patient. He combined many modalities in each treatment, including homeopathy, hydrotherapy, physiotherapy, botanical medicine, nutritional medicine, manipulation, and lifestyle advice.

Dr. Bastyr believed in "complementary medicine" before the word was coined. He used whatever modalities were needed, doing whatever it took to exact a cure. He believed in touching his patients and treated almost everyone with spinal manipulation. By his own admission, 80-90% of his patients were treated with homeopathy. He would frequently combine modalities, treating a patient with electrotherapy and manipulation in the office, and sending them home with vitamins, botanicals or homeopathic remedies. He knew when he was treating acute or chronic disease, and always kept an eye to long range health of his patients, and more importantly, to improving the health of families over the generations.

At Bastyr's memorial service, Jim Ganzini remembered Bastyr in this way:

"In his devotion to keep alive the last school of naturopathy in North America not unlike the last living tree of a species which bears fruit that falls away from the tree, he played a crucial role in propagating the profession which was at that time nearly extinct. He was the root of a profession reaching back as far as any living physician of this era. He gave us a sense of history, longevity, stability and above all, purpose. His having practiced until he could no longer, was not only an inspiration, but showed us that the practice of medicine was a calling, a service, not just a job or a career. He was a leader in natural medicine, not because of politics, but he was the kind of human being we all strive to be."[2]

Carrying the torch through desolate times for alternative medicine in this country, Bastyr taught at nights after a long day of clinical practice. He had a photographic mind, and was an avid student, studying and learning from whomever he could. When he investigated another doctor's treatment, he would incorporate what he could. His studies combined scientific exactness with an open mind. His earliest mentor was C.P. Bryant, with whom he interned at Grace Hospital (See Chapter 5, "Influences and Internships", for more info on Bryant and others mentioned). From him he learned surgery, homeopathy, and obstetrics. He spent six months with O.C. Carroll in Spokane, closing his practice to study with him.

Bastyr investigated everything he came upon, keeping up with scientific research, along with new ideas of a more esoteric nature. If a treatment worked, Bastyr added it to his treatment repertory. Success was his only standard.

Early childhood

John Bartholomew Bastyr was born May 16, 1912, in New Prague, Minnesota. He was born at home to a family from a Bohemian (Czech) background. He was quite young when his family relocated to Fargo, North Dakota, where his early careers included that of farm hand and telegraph boy.[3]

Seattle

In 1928 when Bastyr was a teenager, right before the Great Depression, the family moved to Seattle, Washington, driving a Pike's Peak Chandler automobile, and looking for greener pastures.

Dr. Bastyr's father had a pharmacy at 23rd and Madison.[4] Young John tended the soda fountain there, after school and was the delivery boy as well. It was in this environment he was first exposed to both traditional medicine and botanical medicine.

Education

Bastyr attended Seattle College High School (now Seattle Prep) and graduated in 1929.

His mother was a herbalist and follower of Father Kneipp. She is known to have read Kneipp's books continually. She was also an avid gardener. After young John's appendectomy at the age of nine, his incision opened up (while he was climbing a tree). His mother "went out and got some plantain and put it on the wound."[5]

She later fell ill with gall bladder disease, but avoided surgery when she sought the care of a sanipractic and chiropractor doctor, Harry F. Bonnelle. Dr. Bonnelle was teaching at Seattle College of Chiropractic, and it was he who encouraged Mrs. Bastyr to enroll her son in the college.

After high school, Bastyr went on to study at Seattle College of Chiropractic in Seattle. He graduated on June 26, 1931 and went on to a residency at Grace Hospital that he completed in 1934. He took the Chiropractic Board examination in 1932 and later, the Sanipractic Board examination in 1934.[6]

Bastyr also attended the Northwest College of Chiropractic and was granted a degree on June 5, 1936. He also completed a degree in Surgery, Obstetrics and Internal Medicine, from the University of Guadalajara in June 1944.

Because of the politics between sanipractic and naturopathic licensure, Bastyr first licensure was sanipractic. On October 30,

1957, he was granted a Naturopathic Degree from Grace Hospital. The certificate is signed by C.P. Bryant, President; C.W. Bemis, Secretary; L.W. Squire VP; J D. Craven, Treas. (See Chapter 2.2 "Sanipractic vs. Naturopathic" for more information.)

Dates of Graduation and Certification [7]

Seattle College High School, (now Seattle Prep) – 1929
Seattle College of Chiropractic – June 26, 1931
Northwest College of Chiropractic – Seattle, June 5, 1936 (Signed by Dr. Rohrbacher) Residency at Grace Hospital – 1934 University of Guadalajara. Degree in Surgery, Obstetrics, and Internal Medicine – June 28, 1944

During the time he was at the Seattle College of Chiropractic, he lived in the Wallingford district in Seattle, in the 3500 block of Burke Ave N.[8]

Internship with C.P. Bryant

C. P. Bryant was the head of St Luke's Hospital, now Group Health, and he also ran a homeopathic hospital, Grace Hospital. It was the only "open door" hospital on the West Coast. Any doctor could bring patients there, and treat them as long as he practiced under his licensure. Bryant was the head of surgery there and he was a homeopath as well. Bastyr was the first intern there under Dr. Bryant.

Every weekend, Bryant taught homeopathy. Dr. Larkin of Bellingham also lectured there. The course lasted three years. Classes were held on the third floor of the hospital or in the Polish Hall up the street. Bryant lectured every Sunday for four hours.

Bryant was introduced to homeopathy by Dr. Cooper while attending Jefferson Medical School in Philadephia. After 1906, his wife received homeopathic treatment from Dr Walter James, a student of Adolf Lippe. Bryant's wife had a bad ankle injury and Dr.

James treated her with *Bryonia*. All the swelling went out and she was able to walk again. "That alerted Bryant to homeopathy. By the time he got out to Seattle, he was well into unorthodox treatments."[9] Bryant studied homeopathy with Walter James. He also used physiotherapy and Abrams' Black Box.

In Bryant's homeopathic classes, he discussed individual remedies, and brought cases that he had shown good clinical results. He gave Bastyr books to read, including Farrington's *Clinical Materia Medica*. That copy, containing Bryant's notations, was later given to Bastyr and subsequently donated to the National College of Naturopathic Medicine library.

Dr. Bastyr's first case as an intern was a brain decompression. He aided Bryant as he drilled a hole in the patient's head with a hand drill.

Bryant had a group of sanipratics as interns. They were not required to do a residency, but were drawn because of the access to clinical experience.

Dr. Bryant taught them that "a real student always studies" a lesson Dr. Bastyr followed his whole life. Bryant set another example that Dr. Bastyr followed — Bryant was constantly lobbying the state legislature. One of his causes was against the pasteurization of milk.

Bryant delivered many babies and that is where Dr. Bastyr began his obstetrical training.[10]

Marriage

In 1937, John Bastyr met Aletha Persis LaRoude, an English professor at the University of Washington, while he was a student in her phonetics class. They eloped, keeping their marriage secret for a few months, in order to protect her teaching position. During that time, she kept her wedding ring in a specially made locket.

Together they moved to land in south Redondo Beach near Kent, which they developed into a 4-acre farm. When they first bought the land, they camped out, cutting down trees to build a home. They cleared the land, and put in an orchard and a large garden. The garden became a passion for them both. Their farm animals included chickens, ducks, geese, and many goats, from which Dr. Bastyr enjoyed his goat milk. Bastyr said his "wife was somewhat of a homeopath, too."[11] When their chickens came down with range paralysis, it was her prescription of Lathyrus sativa that saved them. Dr. Bastyr also did his own carpentry work on the house.[12]

Their hobbies included music and dance. Dr. Bastyr played the fiddle and belonged to the Ralston Male Choir and occasionally sang at weddings, directing his songs to his wife. Aletha played the piano and accompanied her husband's fiddle playing. The Bastyrs loved opera, attending Seattle Opera "faithfully."[13] Dr. Bastyr treated many opera singers and was sometimes invited backstage at the Opera House. They were avid dancers, dancing until the last year of her life. The Bastyrs were married for over 52 years until her death in 1989 at the age of 95.

First clinic

Dr. Bastyr's first clinic was in an office downtown, for which he paid $16 a month. It had been the office of his physiology professor, Dr. Royce. Royce also had a clinic on First Hill and he used the downtown office once or twice a week. The office shared a common waiting room with a dentist.

His treatment room contained one adjusting table, which Bastyr had made himself out of an apple box. He attached padding and two armrests and four legs. For an adjustment, the patients would kneel on the floor with their chest on the box.[14]

He practiced in Georgetown and later moved to 10th Avenue E, on Capitol Hill in Seattle. This is where he practiced until he was 81 years old. Much of that time, he drove daily from his 4-acre farm in Kent. Bastyr encouraged young graduates to begin with a low overhead when first starting one's practice as he did himself.[15]

Practice

Dr. Bastyr treated over 50 thousand patients for five generations, over seven decades.[16] He treated some of his patients for over 55 years. "Bastyr became the prototype of the modern naturopathic doctor, who culls the latest findings from the scientific literatures, applies them in ways consistent with naturopathic principles, and verifies the results with appropriate lab studies."[17]

He believed in combining modalities, radiant therapy, manipulation, hydrotherapy, homeopathic remedies, botanicals, with a singular goal: "So you can be most effective.... Each one of us is different and has to be treated individually, whether you are treating them homeopathically or otherwise."[18]

Bastyr delivered hundreds of babies, did underwater births decades ago. He made his own salves, and tinctures, incorporating the new techniques while never forgetting the old.

Even when faced with a very ill patient Dr. Bastyr never gave up. "Always try — sometimes a miracle will occur," he said. "You can't fool yourself if you are treating people.... I used the old beano. I have a fairly photographic memory. I retained a lot of finer points in prescribing."[19]

Educator

He was adept and thorough clinician who readily shared his knowledge.[20]
— JIM GANZINI

Dr. Bastyr was instrumental in creating naturopathic education, as we know it today. Bastyr and his peers carried the torch of alternative medicine for many years, when there were no students, and no new practitioners. They mortgaged their homes to buy a building in which to teach naturopathic medicine to the one or two students a year who would apply. Dr. Bastyr was both grandfather and father to students for the past 20 years, as there was no in-between generation to be our mentors.[21]

In 1954, Western States Chiropractic College in Portland had a two-year, post-graduate program in Naturopathic Medicine. However, in 1955, the National Chiropractic Association decided to accredit only those colleges that granted only chiropractic degrees, and the program at WSCC was discontinued.

National College of Naturopathic Medicine grew from the ashes, incorporated by Frank G. Spaulding, W. Martin Bleything, and Charles R. Stone on May 23, 1956. The school was located in Portland, Oregon, until 1959, when it moved to larger facilities in Seattle. Bastyr was involved in the school from its inception, and when the college moved to Seattle, he became its Executive Director and professor of obstetrics and gynecology. During that same time, he was on the staff of the Thompson Maternity Hospital from 1940 to 1968.[22] Bastyr served as president of the college until retiring in 1979 while retaining the title of President Emeritus until his death.[23] Dr. Bastyr was devoted to NCNM. He continued his commitment to the college. When it moved to Portland, he traveled to teach classes there monthly, through the 1980s.

Dr. Bastyr lectured for hours with few notes. He recalled cases, dosages and treatments, and materia medica of homeopathy and botanicals from memory. Off the top of his head, he would readily quote modern research projects as well as lessons he has been taught himself as a student, decades prior.

For 23 years, he served the students of naturopathy, creating not just a path for all to follow, but a major highway. When Bastyr University was created in 1978, it was named for this illustrious educator.

Naturopathic hospital

"One day we will have our hospitals with gardens in which we will growth organic food and herbs. People will come here to get well."[24]

At one time Bastyr and his colleagues "had a little hospital" called the Greenwood Maternity Hospital. Later on, during the years when NCNM was in Seattle, Bastyr and three colleagues optioned 17 acres and had plans drawn up for a 100-bed hospital at the site. The land bordered a creek and a railroad track. It was to be called a naturopathic rehabilitation sanitarium. Plans included four wings to the building, along with an outside garden. Bastyr envisioned it as a place removed from the city and pollution, in which to rehabilitate people.[25] Their plans fell through but he continued to hope that in the future, the naturopathic community would develop its own hospitals.

Politics

Beginning in 1987, Bastyr served two terms on the Naturopathic Advisory Committee for the Washington State Department of Health. He was an honorary member of the committee until his death.[26]

In the 1970s, he frequently lobbied the Washington State Legislature for the Naturopathic Bill. He enlisted students to drive from Seattle to Olympia with him to meet and encourage the representatives to sign the legislation.[27]

Last years

Dr. Bastyr practiced until his last year of life, seeing up to 30 patients a day. He eventually lived upstairs from his clinic on 10th Ave. in Seattle's Capitol Hill area. He was tended in his last days by his long time office assistant, Diane Wardrip. He passed away in Seattle, Washington, on June 29, 1995, at the age of 83.

A memorial for Dr. Bastyr was held at St. Mark's Cathedral in Seattle, a few blocks from his clinic. The memorial was attended by over 150 people, most of whom had not met him until he was already in his 60s, the age at which most people retire.

Bastyr had big dreams for the future of natural medicine. He dreamed of licensure for naturopaths. He dreamed of training for naturopathic nurse assistants. He dreamed of the creation of a naturopathic hospital. He dreamed of well-trained homeopaths. He dreamed of the science and art of natural medicine working together. When asked about the future of naturopathic medicine, he replied gently, "Keep on with the scientific research, but don't lose the philosophy."[28]

2.
Bastyr and the History of Naturopathy

European roots

Naturopathic roots stem from Father Sebastian Kneipp, a priest in Bavaria who wrote extensively on "Nature Cure." His teachings described the benefits of pure water, fresh air, exercise and herbs. He was famous around the world for his lectures and books on hydrotherapy and healthy living.

Benedict Lust (1872-1945), a German immigrant, came to America in 1892. Following tuberculosis brought on by vaccination, Lust was near death; in fact, his attending doctors signed his death certificate. Lust returned to Germany and was treated by Sebastian Kneipp with the "Kneipp cure" which restored his health. Lust returned to America in 1896 and became Kneipp's official representative.[29]

Lust created a naturopathic sanatorium, a naturopathic college, and a naturopathic magazine.[30] In 1902, he organized the Naturopathic Society of America, later reorganized as the American Naturopathic Association (ANA) in 1919. Two years later, Lust was elected president for life, though the organization split after he died into an Eastern ANA and Western ANA, with different philosophies, organizations and textbooks. The Eastern naturopaths more closely followed Kneipp, and the West tended towards "medicalized" naturopathy."[31] Both Kneipp and Lust influenced Bastyr;

Kneipp's books were well-thumbed in young Bastyr's household. Bastyr became aquatinted with Lust's work while studying with O. G. Carroll in Spokane. Lust visited Carroll at his home and clinic and both Lust and Carroll worked together in the American Naturopathic Association.

Sanipractic vs. Naturopathic

Differences of opinions and legal issues divided the ranks of the naturopaths. Dr. John Lyden. a graduate of Lust's school, the American School of Naturopathy in New York City, termed the word "sanipractic" during a time of in-fighting between the various drugless groups.

In 1919, the Universal Sanipractic College was organized in Seattle, Washington. The word "sanipractic" was defined as the "practice of health" with the keyword "ilimination." Washington state law permitted Sanipractors to practice many healing modalities with the exception of administration of drugs. The students were primarily chiropractors who wanted a more extensive practice.[32]

O. G. Carroll was one of the primary forces of unity between the naturopaths and sanipractics. He wanted to enlist all parties under the banner of Lust and the American Naturopathic Association. Though opposed by his brother Robert, O.G. persisted and eventually succeeded in bringing the groups together. Carroll's was the only listing in their "Drugless Directory" in 1922, and he was the Washington representative to that Association in 1926. He had been nominated to that position by Lust, himself.

National College of Naturopathy

National College Chicago was a spin off from Lindlar's School. Lindlar had come from Germany and was a student of Kneipp, and also Lust in New York. Shoulty and Budden came from Lindlar's Sanitarium in Chicago.

Budden left the school in Chicago and started Western States

College. An attorney and a Ph.D., Budden was very idealistic. The college he started in Seattle taught chiropractic and naturopathy. When Western States decided not to teach naturopathy, NCNM was born.

Drs. Charles Stone, W. Martin Bleything, and Frank Spaulding incorporated National College of Naturopathic Medicine in the state of Oregon.[33] The school started on Hawthorne Blvd, in "a house with a furnace that didn't work"[34] and a clinic on the boulevard. They were at that location for two years, with six to seven students at a time. When college ran into financial troubles, some of the doctors came to the rescue and moved the school to Seattle, where the school stayed until 1974. The first building was one room in what Dr. Bastyr called "the little red schoolhouse."

The profession wanted a school run by the profession, not one man alone, "so they created a board with representatives from each state. "Each had a voice in the operation of the school. It was a very nice idea but each state was highly diversified." Because different states had different requirements for the basic sciences: anatomy, physiology, pathology, or hygiene, or bacteriology, etc., there was a great deal of controversy on the board about the curriculum.

The college building was located at 1329 N. 45th St. in Seattle. The clinic "and classrooms were downstairs, and the library was upstairs. In 1972, when a movement towards more natural methods began, the school had an influx of students. "We had so many we couldn't keep them in that building."[35] The board was presented with an opportunity to move the first two years of basic science training to a college in Kansas that was having financial problems. It was hoped that the students would get quality basic science education while providing tuition money to a struggling institution. However, students felt isolated and missed the contact with naturopaths.

By the late 1970s, "the board decided it was time to head the whole thing back to Portland."[36] The college quickly outgrew their first location on Market Street, and in 1996, the college moved to a Ross Island location in downtown Portland. NCNM has now graduated over 1100 students, who have become practitioners all across the United States and Canada, as well as numerous foreign countries. More than half of the licensed naturopathic physicians practicing in "the United States are graduates of NCNM.

Bastyr University

Dr. Bastyr's continued dedication to NCNM was further brought to fruition with the creation of Bastyr University in Seattle. "Some graduates of NCNM living in Seattle decided they need a local school up there. That brings us here," he was quoted as saying in 1982. [37]

In 1978, the John Bastyr College of Naturopathic Medicine was founded by Les Griffith, Bill Mitchell, and Joseph Pizzorno. Graduating its first class in 1982, this was the first naturopathic college to become accredited by the Northwest Association of Schools and Colleges (NASC).

In 1994 the name was changed to Bastyr University. The college moved to a 50-acre campus in Kenmore, WA. the following year. Under the 22-year leadership of Dr. Pizzorno, the college grew to an enrollment of over 1000, adding undergraduate programs in Nutrition, Psychology, Oriental Medicine, Exercise Science and many more.

Dr. Bastyr's commitment to naturopathic education is being realized today.

3.
Bastyr's Place in the History of Homeopathy

History of homeopathy — Similia similibus curentur

Samuel Hahnemann, founder of homeopathy, first discovered the principle of homeopathy in 1790. While translating Cullen's "Treatise on Materia Medica" Hahnemann began to formulate a new system of medicine. In writing of Peruvian bark, Hahnemann, in a footnote, described for the first time the action of Like Cures Like, observing that, "substances which produce some kind of fever (very strong coffee, pepper, arnica, ignatia bean, arsenic) counteract these types of intermittent fevers." He described his intentional poisoning with the cinchona bark, which caused in him all the symptoms of the malaria that it was known to cure. He deduced, "Peruvian bark, which is used as a remedy for intermittent fever, acts because it can produce symptoms similar to those of intermittent fever in healthy people."[38]

Hahnemann published the first edition of his seminal work, *The Organon of the Medical Art* in 1810.[39] In this volume, he explains his theory of *similia similibus curentur*, which is the basis of homeopathic medicine. The first English edition of this volume was published in 1836. By that time, Constantine Hering, a German student of Hahnemann's, had brought homeopathy to the United States, establishing the Homeopathic Medical College of Pennsylvania, in 1848.

From 1864 -1869, Adolf Lippe was the president of the college. C.P. Bryant consulted with Lippe for treatment of his wife's illness. Upon her cure, Bryant trained in homeopathy at the Homeopathic Medical College of Pennsylvania under Walter James, one of "Lippe's closest students."[40]

Bryant became a leader in the homeopathic movement, as president of the International Hahnemannian Association and *The Homeopathic Recorder*. Dr. Bastyr learned homeopathy from Bryant, while interning with him at Grace Hospital from 1934-1936.

The lineage from Hahnemann, to Lippe, to James, to Bryant, to Bastyr, places Bastyr only five steps from the founding of homeopathy.

4.
History of Medicine and Homeopathy in Washington State

Dr. Alven Bagley was the first homeopathic physician in Seattle. He graduated in 1855 from the Western College of Homeopathic Medicine, and settled in Seattle prior to 1875. In 1865, Dr. Herman Beardsley Bagley graduated from WCHM and moved to Seattle from Michigan, where he had been a surgery professor at Michigan Medical College. He moved to Seattle in 1875 and lived at the northeast corner of Spring St. and Fourth Ave., now the location of the Pacific Plaza Hotel. In 1879, Bagley was given a seat on the city council. He was considered "one of the community's core of brilliant boomers." Bagley died "too suddenly to cure himself" on Feb. 8, 1899.[41]

By 1876, there were four homeopathic practitioners in the state; by 1886, there were eighteen. In 1896, ten years later, there were forty-three, by 1904, fifty-eight. At that time, four were in Dayton, fourteen in Seattle, eleven in Spokane, five in Tacoma, and three in Walla Walla.[42]

The Washington State Homœopathic Medical Society was organized in Seattle in November 1889. The Homœopathic Medical Society of King County was organized in September of the same year.

Maynard Hospital

Doc Maynard was a medical doctor from Ohio who pioneered to Seattle on a wagon train in 1852. He married Catherine Broshears, a widow he met along the trail.

Through his friendship with the native population, Maynard was instrumental in naming the new territory after their leader, Chief Seattle (the other name proposed was Duwamp). Maynard served as King County's first Justice of the Peace and eventually, as School Superintendent. In 1863, Maynard opened Seattle's first hospital, a two-room building on the site of the Elliott Bay Bookstore in present-day Pioneer Square. Maynard practiced medicine there, while his wife served as nurse.[43] Their practice consisted of the early settlers as well as loggers, mill hands, and Indians.[44]

In 1927, the building known from 1933 to 1971 as Maynard's Hospital, was constructed at University and Summit, where Swedish Hospital stands today. It was previously known by a series of names: Dawnland Maternity Inn, North West Hospital, and Martha Washington Hospital. In 1933, it was renamed for the Seattle pioneer, Dr. David S. Maynard. In 1971, Seattle General took ownership and operation of that facility, and the site is now known as the Swedish Hospital Medical Center.

William and Ashley Palmer, were MDs and homeopaths. They started a new hospital where Maynard Hospital, (later called Swedish Hospital) was located. Dr. Bastyr was to do his internship there, but the promoter ran off with the money and they lost the hospital.

Bastyr began interning at Grace Hospital in 1932.

Below are listed homeopathic physicians in Washington before 1886 and the cities in which they practiced.[45]

1852 Day, William W. – Dayton
1855 Bagley, Alven – Seattle
1865 Bagley, Herman B. – Seattle
1868 Booth, H. W. – Cheney
1869 Rice, William H. – Tacoma
1872 Munson, Clinton – Tacoma
1875 Vandervoort, M. – Walla Walla

1875 Whitworth, F. H. – Seattle
1875 Egbert, W. A. – Walla Walla
1875 Mineer, W. S. – Waitsburg
1877 DeVoe, Miss Marmora – Seattle
1880 Penfield, Charles S. – Spokane Falls
1882 Churchill, Frederick A. – Seattle
1883 Mysner, William W. – Tacoma
1883 Capps, William – Centralia
1884 Whitworth, Geo. F., Jr. – Olympia
1886 Simmons, Mrs. N. J. – Waitsburg

5.

Influences and Internships

Elizabeth Peters

Bastyr called Dr. Peters "the matriarch of natural therapy." "Elizabeth Peters was in practice 57 years when I knew her. She had been a student of Kneipp and came from Germany. She told me things that were amazing. She was one of finest women I have ever known."

Peters taught Bastyr how Kneipp gathered plants himself and how he'd diagnose the 10,000 patients he saw each week. He'd watch them go by en masse and determine each one's treatment. The treatment was mainly water therapy as was used by all the pioneers, like O.G. Carroll and Lindlar. Blood tests weren't used but they did culture some things. They used different minerals: grey powders, white powders, black powders, made from bone. They used many different herbs. (Kneipp wrote one of the first herb books.) Peters described how they used different types of hydrotherapy, and different color blankets, and different colors of glass held up for sunlight to go through. The offshoot of this was color therapy and ophthalmic color therapy. "Things were found by trial and error perhaps."

Peters showed Bastyr pictures of her time with Kneipp, such as a photo of Kneipp walking outside in a loose chemise, in order to allow his skin to breathe in the open air. She died in 1958.

"She was a lovely person and I'm sorry I couldn't put it down for posterity."[46]

Adolf Lippe

Lippe was one of the founders of the American school of homeopathy, along with William Wesselhoeft. He was the President of the Homeopathic Medical College of PA from 1864-1869. This college was one of the first institutions to teach homeopathy in the United States. Lippe and Hering both taught at the college. Lippe practiced for fifty years and published about 500 articles.

Graduates of this college included Constantine Lippe, E. A. Farrington, T. L Bradford, E. W. Berridge and Walter James, Swan, Skinner, Richard Phelan (who attended James Tyler Kent's wife and under whom Kent began the study of homeopathy[47]). In 1870, the school merged with the Hahnemann College of Philadelphia.

C.P. Bryant, MD

Bryant was introduced to homeopathy by Adolf Lippe, while he was studying in Philadelphia, Pennsylvania. By 1939, Bryant was president of the International Hahnemannian Association. He was also an editor of *The Homeopathic Recorder.*

A medical doctor, obstetrician, homeopath, and surgeon, Bryant was an eclectic, which caused him to be ostracized from the medical establishment. Bryant had his own way of doing things, for instance, never using gloves to examine a patient, but washing his hands in calendula instead.

About Bryant, Dr. Bastyr said, "Bryant did some remarkable things. When you do things with homeopathy, you are known. He was a good surgeon too."[48] (For more information, see Biography and Homeopathy Chapters.)

I treated over 100 cases of influenza and pneumonia, lost two cases, one who had taken Aspirin for a week when pneumonia developed before I was called; the other a very malignant case with very high temperature from the onset. Remedies: Gelsemium, Eupatorium, Bryonia, etc. — C. P. Bryant, M. D., Seattle [49]

Walter James, MD

James was one of "most stalwart of the Hahnemannian homeopaths" who formed the Lippe Club in Philadelphia along with Lippe and E.J. Lee. The notes of their regular meetings are stored in the Hahnemann Collection at Allegheny University of Health Science, Pennsylvania.[50]

James was the editor of *The Homeopathic Physician,* the official organ for the International Hahnemannian Association (published from1881-1899). The journal had been edited by E.J. Lee and later by G. H. Clark. The journal, which was committed to "Hahnemannian homeopathy," also printed a number of invaluable small repertories.[51]

Charles Littlefield

Dr. Charles Littlefield was a great advocate of the mineral salts, using Schussler's twelve tissue salts, and some others that he discovered himself. He irradiated them with light spectrum to energize, or repotentize them.[52] His book, *The Beginning and Way of Life* [53] published in 1919, describes what he calls, the "practical application of the law of mind control of the mineral salts." Dr. Bastyr met him when they both worked at Grace Hospital.

Dr. Littlefield was able to determine the correct remedy from a urine sample. He collected urine onto a slide, passed it through a flame and it would form a crystal, which he would photograph under a microscope. He was able to diagnose in this manner. Littlefield believed that mineral salts were capable of building pictures within a microscopic area, only 1/32 of an inch. From these slides he was able to diagnosis nutritional deficiencies.

Patients were treated with one or two tissue salts daily, in low potencies. He ground his remedies by hand. He used the remedies nutritionally, believing that they were both foods and "tissue builders of the organism." He called them "physiologic-inorganic foodstuffs." "In no sense of the word are they 'drugs'. They are foods...

Each living thing is a combination of material elements grouped in a manner peculiar to each species."[54]

He pointed out that the oils of lemon, clove, and turpentine are each comprised of the same chemical compound; however, the elements are put together differently. "The law of composition is the law of form." He believed this law to be "the underlying principle of the origin of all living things."

Littlefield believed that man was a dual being: body and mind. Within this duality, the mind itself was also divided into two halves: subjective intelligence (which is the functional processes), and the objective mind (which looks through the five senses onto the external world).

"The human mind is made up of images, just as a forest is made up of trees, or a city of houses. Not all ideas are the result of sensation."[55]

His prescriptions were based on the following: "If patient has mental symptom, physical symptom, and the characteristic aggravation or amelioration of a selected remedy, this is the remedy that will cure."

One time, he and Dr. Bastyr treated a woman with burns over 30% of her body. (Dr. Bastyr did the dressing for Littlefield, according to his instructions.) They treated her only with tissue salts. Her dressings were soaked in liquid tissue salts. She healed completely, with no scarring.

Dr. Bastyr did post mortems for Littlefield, who would not bother with post mortems, because he already knew the cause of death from his observations. Littlefield declared that one patient had died from a kidney complication and when Dr Bastyr did the post mortem, he found that Littlefield's diagnosis had been correct.[56]

O.G. Carroll 1879-1962

Carroll is credited with being the "inventor of constitutional hydrotherapy."[57] Carroll used high dilutions of potencies in isotherapy to treat food allergies. Remedies were made with their potentized blood. He tested the urine to find out what people were allergic to.

Dr. Bastyr was so impressed with Carroll's work that he closed his clinic and spent six months studying with Carroll in 1933 in Spokane, Washington. "I spent six months with O.G. Carroll. I saw 40-50 people a day. Carroll had 10 treatment units, and two girls to apply the compresses."[58] There was a chart on every patient listing the times and areas for treatment, types of compresses, what type of electric modality to apply. Carroll didn't use many body packs, only if the fever was very high. When patients became weak under a fast especially if they were vomiting, they received weak short wave and sine wave stimulation.

Applications varied from 4-10 minutes for hot and 15-20 minutes for the cold. Cold stayed on longer or until it was warm. All compresses were covered with wool and sealed in. Carroll believed there was osmosis between the water in compresses and the patient. The towels became yellowed, especially during a healing crisis.

Carroll used facial diagnosis. For instance, lines coming off the nose under the chin signified rectal or abdominal troubles. He diagnosed Pancreatic lines around the edges of the lips. A raised bump indicates uterine trouble. "People called him psychic, but he was just observing things."

Carroll fasted patients for up to 42 days. He fed them with eyedroppers of water. Carroll tested for allergies using urine, to find what wasn't agreeable to them.[59]

"If I have a difficult case, I will use his (Carroll's) method of analysis. "If you asked him a question 1-1/2 to 2 hours later, you'd get answer. He'd quote 50-60 cases to explain to you."[60]

Bastyr learned iridiagnosis from O.G. Carroll who depended on it. But Bastyr came to the conclusion, "To utilize iris diagnosis alone is foolhardy. Even though some are very good; I don't depend on it."[61]

Carroll was taken to court after one of his patients died, and Bastyr testified at his trial. Carroll won the case.

Carroll brought other doctors into his clinic, including Harold Dick, and Leo Scott.[62]

Carroll was instrumental in reuniting the factions of sanipractic and naturopathic into one licensure. (See 2.1 Sanipractic vs. Naturopathic) Carroll's nephew Robert was one of the founders of NCNM.

Gary Cotton

Cotton was a talented electrotherapist. He used a container with mirrors that reflected in water, focused on the center, when it micronized the tissues. Results were accumulated on slides. Cotton used different parts of the light spectrum and was able to ask questions and get readings from his samples. At one time, he told a man where to find gold in Alaska and he was correct. A map had appeared on the slide. Cotton used mental thought and directed it on the slides.

Schlessie

Schlessie evolved the use of Oxygen 08 therapy.

John Lidden

Sanipractic. His famous treatment was Epsom salts.

Ashley and Willard Palmer

Both of the Palmers were homeopaths. According to Bastyr. "Ashley was a homeopath. Willard was a surgeon and he used homeopathy too." They were at St Luke's, then moved to Northwest and "used the remedies a lot."

> *I treated approximately 500 cases, which included much pneumonia, lost two cases; never used Aspirin nor permitted it to be used. Chief drugs used were Belladonna, Gelsemium, Sticta for the throat symptoms, Mercurius, Natrum muriaticum and Kali muriaticum.* — – A. B. Palmer, M. D., Seattle [63]

William F. Coke

William Coke was a physician, chemist, and homeopath who started working with metabolites, then started the use of Glyoxolide 6x injections, claiming they would start the oxidation reduction process. The injections were given after patient had been prepared with a diet consisting mostly of fruit, but no cherries. (Bastyr loved cherries.)

Coke also used *Parabenzoquinon* 6x for cancer and leukemia. (Pau d'arco has a high content of Parabenzoquinon.) The remedy cost $25 for a 2-cc vial. One had to work rapidly not to get oxidation. Coke also injected *Diazolate* 6x.

Coke observed cycles of threes (3, 6, 9, days) and found that reactions, like flu, or high temperature, would occur in those intervals.

"Coke was 100 years ahead of his time. They are just starting to confirm his ideas now."[64]

Bastyr had one case, a hemorrhaging gastric cancer. He gave the injection every 72 hours three times. The patient lived another 12 years and died of heart attack. The post mortem showed no sign of the cancer. Coke used cycles of 3 6 9 12; oxidation-reduction interval occurred at those intervals.

Dr. Larkin

Dr. Larkin was a homeopath and one of Bastyr's teachers at Grace Hospital. He introduced Dr. Bastyr to some of his favorite books, and gave him some of them, including Mackenzie's *Miracle of Homeopathy*, which Bastyr donated to NCNM.

Herbert Shelton

Herbert Shelton used water fasting for a minimum of 21 days to produce a healing crisis. Shelton believed in food combinations; positive and negative foods were not to be combine together. According to Bastyr, Shelton and the other "old timers" believed that food that grew above and below the ground should not be eaten together. Those growing on the ground could be combined with both.

Arno Koegler

Originally from Germany, Dr. Koegler settled in Waterloo, Ontario Canada. He lectured occasionally at NCNM in the 1970s. Koegler had his own titration method, using a mortar and pestle hooked to a mechanical arm, which ground for hours at a time. He saw up to 100 patients a day. Koegler used iris diagnosis. According to Bastyr, "a lot of the old timers did."[65] Koegler trained John Bender (NCNM 1979), who assumed his practice in Kitchener-Waterloo, Canada, when Koegler died.[66]

Albert Abrams

Albert Abrams is credited with being the inventor or Radionics, though he called his invention "Radio Therapy." His medical training began in Germany, where he graduated first in his class at Heidelberg University. He later taught pathology at Stanford University.

An expert at the art of diagnosis by percussion, he discovered that disease has some kind of energy that can run through an electrical lead. He attached metal discs to the leads and developed a system for diagnosis and to identify disease in a minute area, and to identify pathogens. He named the device "Bio-meter." He thought that if he neutralized the vibrations of diseased cells with this vibration radiator, he could cure diseases. He invented a machine called an "Oscilloclast" with which he said he could demolish diseased energy via a medical technique he called "spondylotherapy,"[67] a version of chiropractic and osteopathy. Abrams claimed that all parts of the body emit electrical impulses with different frequencies that vary with health and disease. He believed he could diagnose disease with his machines, using blood samples and even handwriting samples. And that disease could be treated by using correct vibrations from another of his machines. Abrams developed a total of thirteen devices to diagnose or cure people by matching frequencies.

Bastyr owned an oscilloclast but found he "couldn't get the same answer twice." Bastyr respected Abrams' work, but felt "his students ruined it."[68]

The so-called "Abrams' Black Boxes" were used by over 3,500 practitioners by 1921, but after the death of one of Abrams' patients, he was attacked by the AMA, whom they later, "easily ranked as the dean of twentieth-century charlatans."[69]

Abrams' first research on the subject of radio waves was published years before the radio was invented in 1920. Though Abrams' work was questioned by many, he was also defended by many (including the authors Upton Sinclair and Sir Arthur Conan Doyle). Abrams' work has inspired many future inventors in the field of electrotherapeutics.

Joseph Boucher

Dr. Joseph Boucher lived in British Columbia, Canada, and was a trusted colleague of Dr. Bastyr. For many years, he was President and Secretary of NCNM's Board of Trustees. He was also President of the Association of Naturopathic Physicians of B. C. (1981-1982) and the National Canadian Naturopathic Association. In 2000, a new Canadian Naturopathic College was named from Dr. Boucher.

PHILOSOPHY

6.
Philosophy

At Bastyr's memorial service, Dr. Fernando Vega recalled this conversation. When asked what was the proper scope of naturopathic medicine, Bastyr replied, "Well, everything."

"What do you mean, everything? Drugs?" Vega questioned.

"Yes."

"Surgery?"

"Yes."

"Radiation?"

Bastyr replied, "If that's what it takes. Whatever it takes."[70]

Bastyr understood the limits of healing. He made students take an oath at graduation. "Treat those who come to you and don't treat those who don't come to you."[71]

All of his students were taught to touch their patients. Bastyr believed in the important connection that it made. He advised the students, "You want to learn to use your hands."[72]

Bastyr listened to his patients. In ascertaining progress on a case, Bastyr said that the patient would tell you if you had the right treatment or not. He said that "the patient will tell you, I'm not doing well; you don't have the right remedy, Doc."[73]

Bastyr never gave up on a case. If he did not get the desired results, he used a different method of diagnosis. "If you have case you can't do anything with, don't respond no matter what, and use a different method of diagnosis." Even against impossible odds, he never gave up, thinking, "maybe a miracle will happen."

Recommending the usage of whole glands as opposed to extracts, Bastyr noted that using a portion of the gland could cause problems because, "The body doesn't work that way." He viewed the body as a totality. "You have to take the patient as a whole."

Bastyr understood the body as totality. He would point out that a "migraine is expression of the liver,"[74] or commenting that "If you have a low acetic saliva, you have a low hydrochloric acid."[75] Or noting that "the formation of salivary glands is similar to that of pancreatic glands."[76] He stated that most degenerative disease starts in liver.[77]

Bastyr understood that there was not always a linear path to healing, saying "A doesn't always equal B you have go through C and maybe D before you get to B."[78] He was a fan of logic. "We do not want to become fanatical. We want to have reserve, we want to have common sense, we should have good judgement too."[79]

It is important to know if you are helping the patient or driving their disease inward. Taken from Hering's Law, Bastyr understood the healing principles that stated that during healing, symptoms returned in reverse order to their appearance, symptoms would disappear from within outward, and from above downward.

Bastyr also taught students to watch out for the effects of a healing crisis. He knew that you didn't cure or complete the cure, or you could cause suppression. Dr. Bastyr tells a story about an infertile patient who ate a great deal of sugar. He told her to stop eating sugar. After a few days she developed a cold. She did not "catch" a cold. The cold was caused by her body eliminating the sugar.[80] Healing crises can be brought on by hydrotherapy, chiropractic, or physiotherapy. Whatever modality you use, "If you stop the reaction, you drive things inwards and get a more chronic condition or a drop in vitality."

Bastyr used intuition as well as science to guide him. And he also believed strongly in the power of words. He practiced hypnotherapy, especially in obstetrical cases, and used the power of positive thinking. "If you don't believe in what you are doing and patient won't believe in what you are doing, the patient will not get well."[81]

Even knowing the power of words, he was a realist. He was not swayed by inflated ideas, even his own. "When I got out of school, I could cure anybody and everything. I found out shortly that you couldn't. You had limitations. Always remember to be circumspect. Do the best you can. A lot of times it's a lot better than anything else."[82]

The body adapted and he changed his therapies to adapt with his patients. "I don't think anything should be continued for the lifetime of the patient. The body changes constantly. Question is if you are changing it for the better or the worse. "[83] "Any medication you give for a prolonged time should be given rest periods. I don't care what you give them: vitamin A, B or anything. You should change. Why? What does nature do? She changes with the season. The animals change eating habits, sleeping habits, so you too have to do this."[84]

He was an optimist, but he knew the body's limits. He believed there was a chance for regeneration of all tissue, but understood that nerve and cartilage were the slowest to heal.[85]

Bastyr had many patients who lived for years in spite of and with grave disease conditions. Concerning a patient with a lifelong goiter who lived to the age of 90, Bastyr commented, "What are you treating them for? Are you treating them to remove the goiter, to make them feel better, are you treating to be functional?"[86]

Diagnosis was not the cure. Bastyr understood that "diagnosis is important in order to understand the possibilities of what is going to happen to a person." Bastyr believed that "The use of diagnosis is very important. But the diagnosis doesn't always determine the therapy, whether you use more natural laws, botanical, acupuncture, homeopathy, or straight nutrition, manipulation. Diagnosis tells you if you can accomplish something in this patient who has certain pathology. You need to know pathology. This is how you apply principles to natural law."[87]

Bastyr kept ahead of the science. He was aware of the effects of

glucosomine condroitin in the early 1980s, decades before its popu-
larity,[88] and he searched for the nutritional pathways of vitamins
and herbs before that was well understood. He also worked with
radiotherapy before the most people had radios.

He looked forward to the time when there would be more doc-
umentation in the field of natural medicine. "We sadly lack doc-
umentation of our field." He made many suggestions of research
projects. (See Suggestions for Research Chapter.)

He approached the challenge of treating patients with unlim-
ited energy, yet knew his limits. "You have to do it all. No one thing
does everything. I wish there were. You don't cure the world you
help the world turn a little bit."[89]

> *One day, in his clinic, he asked me if I was pregnant.*
> *"No," I said.*
> *"Well, it says here that you are going to be pregnant in July, he*
> *said, looking at my chart.*
> *Later, I found out I had been pregnant at that visit, and I said to*
> *him, "Dr. Bastyr, do you have a hotline to God?"*
> *"Well", he said, " Well, yes I do."*[90]

Role of a healer

Dr. Bastyr understood the limits of his work and what is meant to
be a healer. Though he worked tirelessly for others, he knew it was
their vital force that was doing the work. His intent was not to heal
everyone, but to aid the suffering. Knowing a case was terminal, he
often treated patient up to the time of their death, intent on healing
the suffering and alleviating the pain.

He deemed a case successful if he was able to "help a patient
go through trying times." To help a patient up to the end, "that's a
success."[91]

"Talk to your patient and get him interested in himself, in what
you are doing. You work with them. You teach them how to live
you change their lifestyle. You give them hope, motivation to get

better. This is why clinical setting is important."[92]

"No healing takes place unless it is by nature itself and the body itself. Unless it has insurmountable odds, it will generally succeed in doing just that."[93]

He believed that it was his responsibility to help a patient's state of mind. He would encourage them, believing that they needed the will to fight, to combat, to get well. They needed to feel they were going to get well.

Humor

Dr. Bastyr had a great sense of humor, frequently making jokes at his own expense, such as, "My writing is not conducive to reading."[94]

Dr. Bastyr once asked students if they knew how to make a tenth of a drop of tincture. Fortunately, none of the students fell into the trap of his trick question. "Why, you take a drop and separate it into 10 parts," he joked. While the befuddled students pondered this, Dr. Bastyr laughed and finally explained that the proper way to obtain a tenth of a drop was to add 10 times more liquid. For instance, if a recipe called for a tenth drop of tincture to a dram, instead, one drop would be added to 10 drams.

Bastyr told me a story about his early chiropractic days. (I believe he was still studying in college at the time.) A strange dog came to the door of his basement office. He asked the dog if it wanted an adjustment and it wagged its tale. Bastyr adjusted the dog, and the following day, it returned, apparently wanting another adjustment. [95]

Bastyr comments were often humorous and insightful. In telling students about an herbal formula, Dr. Bastyr suggested that it would, "wake a dead man. Give a half teaspoon of that and follow with chases of cold water and he'll rise up off the floor. You should always try this on the dog, you being the dog, to experience how these things act. You should try them on yourself. I've been very sick many times because of what I did."[96]

In recommending manipulation for a patient, Bastyr suggested, "Break them in gently, you know."[97]

7.

Advice To Students

Dr. Bastyr was very generous to students, as well as being a fascinating and often humorous storyteller. From the top of his head, with no notes in front of him, he could report details of cases from decades before, including lab tests, treatments used, and frequency of dosages. Most importantly, he shared of himself, his heart, his dreams for the future, and his encouragement both for the students on their journey of knowledge, and for the path of naturopathic medicine.

Bastyr believed in learning one new fact a day. "Don't stop studying. Make it a part of your life.... Facts we learned 10 years ago are no longer facts. So many things to learn. So many things to remember. When you are young you'll be able to do that. If you don't use it you'll lose it. Use all your senses. This is how you become aquatinted with the outside world." His advice to students was "It's a question of attitude and if you apply yourself. Organize your knowledge."[98]

He was known to study one remedy a night before he went to sleep. He enjoined his students to do the same. "Study the remedies every night. Each remedy has its own particular characteristics. You read them over and over, and then you see something you never saw before."[99]

Along with knowledge, Bastyr enjoined students to have confidence. "You first have to believe in what you are doing. You have to believe you can do things with what you have learned. You must have confidence that what you do is going to help the patient.

Apply the knowledge by continuing to learn something. That's the background of facts that you can apply therapeutically."[100]

Bastyr had great awe for the human body. He felt that you understood creation by understanding the body. "The body is a very beautiful thing. It astounds you. We know very little about a great many things. We think we know a lot but alongside the peaks of knowledge there are great ridges."[101]

Bastyr claims that it took him six months to "figure out which end of the body was which." He believed in relating each symptom to another so the body appeared as a whole and you could see the functions of physiology, anatomy, biology, and chemistry. "See patient as they actually are. It isn't that you treat a patient because he is there. You try to understand the patient, relate to them, and have rapport. You should be able to put yourself in patient's place. Then you relate back and forth."[102]

Bastyr believed that students should have basic core knowledge of all types of therapeutics, then specialize later. He thought that residency was a good way to learn. Learning on your own, while possible, he felt was difficult.

He was fond of telling stories about the "old timers", doctors whose roots went back to Europe, to Kneipp, Hahnemann, and Lust. Bastyr's stories, like so much about his place in history, bridges the time between the nature doctors of old and modern homeopathy. His stories recall Elizabeth Peters, O.G. Carroll, the Abrams' Box, iridiagnosis, and more than anything else, hydrotherapy, the modality used by many of the early Nature Doctors.

This is what he learned from their cumulative knowledge.

"Lots of docs have different opinions. The number of docs in a room equals the number of opinions… Old docs were in business of getting people well. That is what we try to cultivate. There has to be diversity in our profession. You can become teachers, or researches or practitioners."[103]

Bastyr recommended that students read the older books and journals. "They are valuable in understanding what they were thinking." He suggested homeopathic literature, for information on laws of healing, suggesting that Kent's Philosophy was a good book to study.[104] He also recommended books by Henry Lindlar, Lahn, Goodinall, Ellingwood, Fox, Webb, Coffin, Hering, Knowle, Clineman. He also advised reading books by Rosecrusians and Rudolf Steiner, especially his method of biodynamic gardening and the "life of the soil."[105]

"Organize your knowledge. Apply the knowledge by continuing to learn something. That's the background of facts that you can apply therapeutically."[106]

Joe Pizzorno, founder of Bastyr University, has said that Dr. Bastyr taught him two things, "how quickly the body can heal" and "the power of relentless study."[107]

Bastyr's hopes for the students included, "I hope you'll learn to live the natural way,"[108] and "Never stop studying. You have to keep learning."[109]

PRACTICE & MODALITIES

8.
Homeopathy

"Basically I may be somewhat eclectic, but I am a homeopath. I really believe in it fellows. So we still use it"[110]

Dr. Bastyr considered himself a homeopath. Whenever he lectured for more than a few minutes he mentioned homeopathy. He used homeopathy in nearly every case that came in, and said, "Eighty to ninety percent get homeopathic treatment at some time."[111] He used homeopathic philosophies in the way he evaluated his patients and his practice, and he enjoined his students to study homeopathy "in depth." As much of his practice and philosophy was devoted to homeopathy and large quantities of his clinical notes relate to homeopathy, this chapter delves into his practice of homeopathy at length.

Bastyr was part of the early homeopathic heritage in the United States. His personal contribution to homeopathy has been lost until now. Bastyr's practice of homeopathy provides us with a view into an early practitioner of homeopathy in the United States.

Bastyr's study of homeopathy followed his training in chiropractic and sanipractic. He and others of his time combined these modalities and created an important connection between them for naturopathic medicine. But Bastyr was unique because he trained extensively with a surgeon who used homeopathy in a hospital setting, to surgery, in obstetrics, and as a family doctor. Bastyr was deepened in the most classical homeopathic education available at the time.

From Hahnemann to Lippe, to James, to Bryant, Bastyr was only five steps away from the founder of homeopathy.

Most homeopaths in Bastyr's time were educated in homeopathic colleges. Most of the chiropractors and naturopaths were trained in colleges teaching those specialties. But Bastyr bridged that gap. Bastyr was exceptionally well-trained in homeopathy, compared to his peers, whose formal training was geared more towards hydrotherapy and nutrition. According to Julian Winston, "Bastyr's education was unique in that he had good homeopathic mentors."[112] Because he was fascinated by homeopathy and used it consistently and successfully in his practice, homeopathy has become a vital part of the naturopathic tradition.

> *Bastyr's conversion to homeopathy was an important move for the modern naturopathic profession. Homeopathy had been part of naturopathic medicine for decades, but its role had been much more peripheral. The majority of practitioners had not received such intensive, classical instruction as Bastyr. In the 1950's when Bastyr became involved in establishing and teaching a naturopathic curriculum, his balanced emphasis of homeopathy as a therapeutic modality coequal with nutrition, hydrotherapy and botanical medicine assured its place in the ongoing development of naturopathic science.* [113]

Classically trained, Bastyr was both a low and high potency prescriber. He used homeopathy to treat both acute and chronic disease, as well as using homeopathy prophylactically to prevent diseases like polio and pertussis. He used nosodes, isopathy, and even made his own remedies. He studied one remedy a night, from books he kept by his bedside, frequently Farrington's *Materia Medica*.

He used homeopathy frequently during childbirth and with children, whom he found like to take the remedies. He successfully treated breast cancer, and polio, with homeopathy. He used homeopathy from birth to death, treating women for infertility, turning infants in utero, and using homeopathy to soothe the pains of elderly and terminal patients.

Bastyr used constitutional homeopathy, as we know it today, as well as treating acute diseases in a manner currently called "homeospecific," i.e., the use of specific remedies for specific disease conditions. An example is using *Arsenicum iodatum* (2x) for bronchitis.

For classical prescriptions based on constitution, he relied on the totality of the remedy. "Each remedy is a person and you soon become acquainted with them. See people; don't memorize a list of symptoms. This gives you insight into remedies. This is useful in diagnosis."[114]

The pharmacy in his clinic was filled with liquid bottles from which he would medicate pellets to fill prescriptions. He purchased the remedies from Boericke and Tafel, Luyties, Standard, Dolisos. Dr. Bastyr also used Schussler's tissue salts.

"I think every student should have a core knowledge of homeopathy," said Bastyr in 1983. Bastyr understood the amount of study it took to be a homeopath. "We have quite a few remedies of course, and they do run the gamut."[115] To be a competent homeopath, Dr. Bastyr recommended three hours of classes for three years, a total of nine courses. This, he believed, would generate a "core understanding" of homeopathy. "You can't learn it in a week. It's a constant study."[116]

Bastyr was involved in medical politics in the beginning of his studies, attending meetings of the International Hahnemannian Society. He also attended meetings of the West Coast Hahnemann Society, with his mentor, Bryant, who had been a past president of the IHA from 1938 to 1939.

Bastyr enjoined his colleagues and students to use homeopathy. When other physicians referred cases to Bastyr for homeopathy consultation, he tried to get them to learn to use homeopathy themselves. He advised, "You must have confidence in what you do and in the remedies too."[117]

Homeopathic Philosophy: Hering's Laws of Cure

Even when not practicing homeopathy, Bastyr used Hering's Laws of Cure and homeopathic perspectives to access the progress of a case.

Hering's Laws of Cure state that cure will take place from above downward, from the inside out, and from organs of more importance to the less important, and that symptoms will return in the reverse order of their appearance. Homeopathic philosophy looks for the totality, and not just the symptoms or the disease. In Bastyr's practice, he thought in homeopathic terms, looking for the totality, even when treating with botanicals, manipulation, or hydrotherapy.

For instance, thinking as a homeopath, Bastyr explained that skin conditions were not cured by localized treatments alone, because the whole person needed to be treated, not just the skin. The disease was not in the skin, but in the totality of the person. He explained that this was why "homeopaths decry the use of local applications."[118]

Dr. Bastyr's Conversion to Homeopathy:
First cases

When Dr. Bastyr was interning at Grace Hospital, he was also working in his father's pharmacy at 23rd and Madison Street, in Seattle. His father had become interested in homeopathy through his son.

One day a woman came to the pharmacy with a bladder infection. She asked for something for the bladder infection but had already taken all the traditional medicines they had to offer. The woman was chilly and crying, and in great pain. She felt pressure, and described her condition as follows. "If I don't sit here with my leg crossed everything will fall out." Dr. Bastyr happened to be nearby, studying the remedy *Sepia* from Farrington's *Materia Medica*. He asked the woman if she would mind taking some powders. There would be no charge, and all she had to do was to report back on how she was doing. She said she would take anything if it would help. Bastyr gave her four powders of *Sepia* 200c to take one hour apart. The method of dosage was Bryant's traditional way of giving remedies, by a divided dose.

The woman returned the next day and said, "What did you give me? I don't have to sit in front of the fire. I have no pain and don't leak all over the place." Bastyr noted that Farrington had described her to perfection.

Bastyr felt he had witnessed "something magic. My eyes opened up. This is one of the first things that convinced me there was something in the remedies."

A week later, a gentleman came in with intersecting ringworm all over his face. He had tried all the treatments that were existent at that time. Bastyr again provided homeopathic remedies and two days later; the face was almost completely healed. "That impressed me so tremendously of what the remedies would do."[119]

Another early case was a hysterical, grief stricken woman who responded quickly to *Ignatia* 200c. "Inside a half hour, she was back talking perfectly normal. So many things have happened like that."[120]

These early cases convinced Bastyr of the efficacy of homeopathy and that, "All patients respond if you get the right remedy."

Constitutional homeopathy and miasmatic prescribing

Bastyr treated both acute and chronic disease with homeopathy. He understood that a person's constitution was the deepest source of both disease and healing and looked for the constitutional homeopathic remedy whenever he could. He understood that a homeopathic remedy could change the background, or "the soil in which things grow."

According to homeopathic philosophy, an acute disease can sometimes be the visible tip of an iceberg. The underlying constitutional disease must be treated in order of a complete cure to take place. In these situations, he would use a remedy for a chronic problem, rather than treat the acute symptoms. "Sometimes a constitutional remedy will clear up an acute right away."

Miasms

The homeopathic philosophy of miasms explains that a person can inherit a disease state left over from their ancestors. For instance, if a person has tuberculosis, their progeny will carry the so-called tubercular miasm, a kind of taint that blocks health. Bastyr felt that "Kent describes miasms fairly accurately." And felt there were even more miasms than the ones he mentioned.

Bastyr knew he could remove the miasms, thereby changing the "soil" and improving a person's health. "You can do tremendous things with a homeopathy remedy. But it takes time. You can change an individual's background chemistry." But he warned, "You needed time to do this."

Acute vs. chronic

The timing of the constitutional remedy is important. Bastyr recommended, "If you haven't had the patient before, use the acute indicated remedy, even if the constitutional is apparent. Give the constitutional later. If you have well indicated acute of a different remedy, give that. Don't give a constitutional remedy to a new patient…. If you haven't had the patient before, use the acute remedy first. It takes a good deal of long hard study to get the whole picture so you can lop off all of them at once, and that is pretty hard to do."

He felt that a new patient would not be forthcoming with important chronic symptoms. On a second or follow-up visit, additional constitutional symptoms would come out that deepen your understanding of the depth of the case. "It takes a good deal of good hard study to get the whole picture," said Bastyr. "If they come in with immediate symptoms, Like 'my nose is red and I want it white', you treat that."

Bastyr understood the importance of searching for the source of disease. Even when treating acute symptom, like allergies, Bastyr used constitutional homeopathy. "If they are aware that certain symptoms come on with foods, hives, nasal, you can still get constitutional symptoms to find a remedy." In those instances, he found that even eliminating the symptoms from the allergy, what homeopaths call the "modalities," you could still find enough other symptoms to prescribe homeopathically. "Even if it eliminated modalities you would use for constitutional prescription, it would not eliminate enough of them to change the prescription.... You use higher potency to constitutionally change the chemistry, the background, the soil that is behind it all."

In treating acute problems, if he was sure of the simillimum he believed in using the high potency because "it will act quickly. If you are not sure, use low and repeat frequently."[121]

Potency

Bastyr used low, high and intermediate potencies, following what he had been taught by his different teachers Bastyr considered tincture to 12x as low potency, and 30c to 200c and up as high potency. He did not consider himself a "one potency man," and used remedies up to CM. Bastyr advised homeopaths to use all the potencies and the tinctures as well. "Potency depends on individual."[122]

In the history of homeopathy, there had been an ongoing division between the high and low potency prescribers. John Renner used low potencies, combos and 30s. Nash started with low potencies then went higher. Swan, Finke, Grimmer, and Kent all used high potencies. "Some were converted because of the rapidity with which they (high potency remedies) actually worked," Bastyr said.[123]

Bastyr understood the history of this division, stating, "Some of the men were divided between the low potency men and the high potency men. But in Hahnemann's time they worked with tincture and a high potency was 30c."[124] Bastyr was educated by a man who had no preconceived ideas, and who taught him both high and low potency prescribing. He learned to use all the potencies when applicable. "Dr. Bryant taught me to run the gamut. He'd go up and down, depending on what he had."[125]

"If you use high potency, you are shooting with a rifle. Low potency, you are shooting with a shotgun...." Bryant taught that the homeopath needed to look for symptoms representing the three legs of a stool. "You have to have three good symptoms to sit on the stool. If you have three good symptoms with good modalities, then you can use the higher potencies. If there are concomitants or they are inimical, or you are not sure of the remedy, use lower. But if you have three characteristic symptoms or keynote symptoms, you can use a higher potency. But if you can't decide which remedy, use the lower potency."[126]

Potency selection also depended on the type of patient, as well as what you wanted to treat. Body typology had a say in Bastyr's potency choice as well. As in everything in homeopathy, prescription was based on the individual. "I can't give you any hard and fast rules. It depends on the patient.... The action will vary. If you have a low-level energy type of patient, a phlegmatic type of patient, you will probably get better results with low potency. For a highly nervous or sensitive individual, use high potencies."[127]

In cases of patients who have large pathological changes, be careful with high potencies, in case "a person's vital force is not sufficient to survive the aggravation, anymore than if you use hydrotherapy. There is a limit to what the body can respond to." If there are structural changes be careful. Nosodes, metals, *Sulphur* too. *Arsenicum, Lachesis, Phosphorus* can induce euthanasia.[128]

Too high a potency will produce an aggravation that can have the opposite effect. In that case, Bastyr advised, "give a low potency and that will smooth it right out."

Some remedies function differently depending on potency. For instance, Bastyr found that in the lower potencies, *Silica* or *Mercury viv* or *Mercury corr*, would "bring something to a head" causing suppuration, whereas the high potencies caused absorption. Small variations of potency could cause these different functions, for instance, deciding between a "3x or 6x will make the difference between suppuration and absorption."

Certain conditions required a high or low potency. For example, Bastyr found the higher potencies were more useful for treating bony involvement, in prescriptions of *Calc fluor* or *Fluoric acid*.

Bastyr read in an old British, homeopathic journal that *Lycopodium* did not express its antipsoric qualities below 30c. Below that, it had effects on the digestive tract, but for constitutional work and to change the antipsoric state, Bastyr prescribed above 30c.[129]

Potency choice also depended on frequency of dose. Bastyr treated with low potency when he had a case that required more frequent repetition, because he found that the low potencies bore repeating without causing any problems.

Remedy action

Though it varies by individual, Bastyr was taught that a 6x lasted four to six hours; a 2c to 30c lasted four to ten days; a 200c lasted two weeks to a month. Higher than that lasted longer. That being said, he had seen a 6x act for many years. How do you account for action of a 6x acting for two years? Ever the scientist, yet ever the pragmatist, Bastyr advised, "You have to reconcile yourself."

Bastyr knew that some of the opponents of homeopathy pointed to the length of action of an immeasurable dose as proof that homeopathy could not work. "It's hard to believe that you can give one remedy and ten months later your remedy is still acting."

"One of the oppositions to homeopathy has been because this doesn't sound right. It really doesn't sound right, that one remedy would act that long. I've seen it act in a 6x for a period in two years. How do you explain that a 10M or MM would also act that long? How do you recognize that this action is going on? Is it a modification that is going on in an aggravation? I can't say that a remedy doesn't act for certain lengths of time because we know it does."[130]

Research is needed to answer many questions in homeopathy

and Bastyr always encouraged his students in research. What is the action of the remedy and how do you recognize it? What goes on during an aggravation? Is that a modification of the original action of the remedy? [131]

Bastyr knew that the science of his time could not answer these questions. He believed in homeopathy because he saw the results. He trusted that future naturopaths and homeopaths would find the pathways and quell the doubts of the disbelievers.

Bastyr used tinctures as well as potentized medicines. He understood that some remedies were more toxic in mother tincture than in potency, for instance, Arsenic. He also determined that tinctures had a partial physiological effect, depending on the amount used. Unlike potentized remedies, the size of the dose impacted the effect of the tinctures. The larger the doses of mother tincture the larger the physiological effects.

For either tinctures or homeopathy, Dr. Bastyr believed in the minimum dose. "Use symptomatology to guide you about what you want to use. Don't use huge doses."

Bastyr was taught that certain remedies didn't hold their potency over periods of time. Aromatics are more likely to lose potency. He never bought more than 16 oz of Pulsatilla at a time, having been taught that after a year, it would not be effective. "Don't buy huge quantities of things. Keep them in effective form."

Bastyr kept his high potency remedies separate from other remedies, as had his teachers.[132] At that time, this was common practice. Boericke and Tafel shipped remedies in cardboard boxes with divisions in between that did not allow bottles to touch each other. Certain remedies had more effect on the others. For instance, he advised keeping camphor away from other vegetable remedies.

Nosodes and homeoprophylaxis

Nosodes are used to clear the constitution of miasmatic or inherited conditions or to prevent disease. Bastyr was well aware of the blocks to health that miasms could cause. He used nosodes to change the constitution and for autoimmune symptoms. He frequently used *Bacillinum, Psorinum,* and *Scirrhinum* to clear a case. [133] He used *Tuberculinum* if the lymphatic were involved and frequently in cases of infertility.[134] As a homeoprophylaxis, to prevent disease, he used *Pertussin, Variolinum, Pituitary, Diptherinum, Scarlatina, Morbellinum,* and *Lathyrus sativa.*[135] He also used nosodes to treat skin conditions:

"In homeopathic literature they have used nosodes for years."

Bastyr treated the children he delivered for four months after their birth, for postnatal care. During this time, he gave them nosodes such as *Variolinum, Diptherinum* instead of vaccinations.[136] "I've never had a kid with *diphtheria,* or polio. They never did develop it." He used *Lathyrus* 30c in all of his pediatric cases, and never had a case of polio in any of his pediatric cases. Another doctor brought a twelve-year-old child with polio to Bastyr. He put him on *Lathyrus* and the child recovered with no residual paralysis.

In one instance, during an outbreak of whooping cough at an elementary school, the mother of a newborn baby sought Dr. Bastyr's advice. He recommended *Pertussin* 30c daily, during the "wet" season. The infant never came down with whooping cough, though his older brother did.[137]

He recommended that all students read Compton-Burnett on use of nosodes. "I think he's one of the best."[138] Use of nosodes and of intercurrent remedies that are well indicated whether in allergy or chronic recurring infections, or bad immune system is recommended.

Bastyr prescribed the nosodes *Bacillinum,* for skin rashes and enlarged tonsils, for weak, whiny kids, with cervical adenopathy, pale, when the rash was aggravated on becoming heated. He found *Bacillinum* also useful for children who came down with recurring colds. He stated that Bacillinum would "do something to their vitality" to activate their immune systems.[139] He also used constitutional nosodes for hyperactive kids.[140] He found Bacillinum was well indicated in cases of mononucleosis.

Bastyr counseled, "Don't repeat nosodes too frequently." If you repeat a nosode too often, you will aggravate the case. He advised repetition no oftener than once a month or every three months. If you repeat a nosode too often, you will aggravate the case, as described by Compton-Burnett. "You will fix the patient so they won't' respond to a remedy."[141]

He rarely used nosodes below 30c, and frequently used 200c. The exception was in cases of staph or strep infections, when he used as low as 12c. For instance, he used repeated doses of *Strep* 12c in cases of constant, repetitive, strep infections.

He used his understanding of remedy pictures and typology in his nosode prescribing as well. He described those needing *Tuberculinum* and *Bacillinum* as "pale people." And found that *Calcarea carb* can be easily confused with *Tuberculinum* and that *Calc phos* can appear like a *Bacillinum* patient.

In his continued quest for scientific evidence, Bastyr searched for the reason for the action of the nosodes. He speculated that the nosode action was to be found in changes that they generated in the immune system. He speculated that the remedies might assist in the formation and release in receptor sites of the lymph cells that change them so body can recognize invaders. "This is where answers will come. If we had electron microscope so you can see change in the intracellular structure, this is where we are going to go."[142]

Bryant's divided dose

Bryant's method of dosing consisted in what he called a "divided dose." He made up four packets combining *Sac lac* (milk sugar) with a few medicated pellets, usually #10 size. The patient was given four packets to take every four hours. To follow that, they were given drops that contained only placebo.

Plussing

When a patient's response wasn't as it should be, Bastyr advised using another remedy, or changing potency, particularly if the patient was getting worse. "Clinically, if you give a well-indicated remedy and there is no change in patient, either you are giving the wrong remedy or the remedy is not working."[143] If same remedy seems indicated but the remedy didn't cause changes, he advised going up to next potency. For example, he would start dosage at 30c, then go up to a 200c, the next day. If there were no reaction the second day, he would go back down.

Dr. Bastyr also described the treatment known as plussing used by the "old timers." They prescribed only one remedy, but changed the potency each day, starting with a 30c on day one, 200 the next, 1M the next, up to CM. "Some claimed tremendous results."[144]

Repeating doses

Bastyr expected a 30c dose to last at least three to four weeks. He found that if a patient is exposed to a great many things and taking a lot of things, the remedy would need to be repeated. "The more things a patient is exposed to, they dull the remedy. You may have to repeat more frequently."[145]

Sometimes Bastyr started a prescription with a single dose on the tongue. But because of the environment, he found that frequently, one dose would not start a remedy. When he used a high potency (any remedy 30c or above) he gave the remedy in four doses, one hourly.

Remedy reaction/aggravation

A woman came to see Dr. Bastyr for a stomach problem. He gave her Sulphur CM. Her stomach cleared up but a rash developed "from head to foot."[146]

"If your remedy is not exact you will get a reaction too, not in the symptoms that they have, but in symptoms of the remedy. The higher the potency, the deeper the aggravation. High potencies will also react with the previous remedies that they've had."

He found that most aggravations from a remedy occurred within three to five days especially when dealing with high potencies (above 30c).

Pharmacy

Bryant had some of Kent's original remedies. He gave some to Bastyr who continued to use them throughout his years in practice, claiming he still had some of Kent's remedies into the 1980s. Most of them are higher potency. The remedies from Kent were #10 pellets medicated with tincture. Lachesis 8x was a favorite potency of Kent and Dr. Bastyr had some of that.[147]

Bastyr's pharmacy consisted mainly of liquid potencies, from which he medicated pellets as needed. He also grafted remedies by diluting them and then adding them to blank pellets of sac lac (milk sugar). He felt that the pellets dried out, which is why he kept the liquid potencies, but he claimed that dried out pellets could be reactivated by adding alcohol.

Remedies in Bastyr's clinic were purchased from Erhardt and Karl, Boericke and Tafel, and Luyties. He used Weise Homeopathic Pharmacy in Kansas City (AKA K. C. Homeopathic Pharmacy, 111 Wyandottie St. Kansas City, MO) and Chicago Pharmacy Co. [148]

Provings

Dr. Bastyr understood the value of provings. He studied provings to learn better understanding of the remedies, and also understood the value of conducting provings as a learning tool themselves. He enjoined students to participate in provings. "Your class should do a proving. That's one way you can learn to get the essence of a remedy."[149]

Combination remedies

Dr. Bastyr used combination remedies from Luyties and Boericke and Tafel pharmacies and Hyland's. If he knew the constitutional remedy, he would use it. But if he only had a few characteristics, he would use an acute remedy, or a combination remedy. "Some of them are OK to use. If you are in a hurry and can't get symptoms out of patient, give them this to take until we question them more. By the next visit they tell you symptoms they were not remembering. The first interview doesn't always give you a remedy. Many times you can do this."[150]

Placebo usage

Dr. Bastyr used placebo when necessary. He understood that the patient wanted to feel they were doing something to help themselves. Patients who were educated in "pure homeopathy" understood the need to wait for the remedy action, but the average patient did not. "The remedy is still going to work with fantastic results."[151]

How remedies act

Bastyr believed that the possible background to the action of the remedies was in changes that the remedies caused in the immune system. He postulated that the formation and release in receptor sites of lymph cells changed it so body could recognize invaders. "This is where answers will come. If we had electron microscope you could see changes in intracellular structure. This is where we are going to go."[152]

Measuring results

One of Bastyr's colleagues, Guy Beckley Stearns, tested the remedies on patients by bringing the remedy to the temple of the patient, without them seeing what he was doing. Stern believed that the pupil would dilate if the correct remedy was selected. [153] Others tried measuring the coagulation of the serum of an individual.

Bastyr's criterion was simple. "If you give a remedy the symptoms will change. That's how you know – if there are results. You have to have some criterion to go by. If not you don't have the right remedy."" [154]

Combining Modalities

Bastyr used homeopathy along with many other modalities. He cared only about results, not theories. His standard was, "Is the patient better? Are the symptoms relieved? Is he functioning better?" He said, "There is the purist and there is the practical." [155] And he was only interested in getting results Bastyr didn't care to prove that a substance had the effect he desired. His only concern was the improved health of the patient.

A student once asked him how he knew which of the many modalities was working? He responded, "I don't think you do. Is the patient better? That is the question. How is your patient doing? Is he improving? How is his mentality? Are the symptoms relieved? Is he functioning better?" [156]

"In higher potency, the cycle (of healing) is going to start, no matter what you do. To be pure, it is better not to use other treatments." Though acupuncture or vitamins given on the same day as the remedy was started could antidote a remedy, he felt that hydrotherapy did not interfere in any way. [157] For those patients who needed to feel they were doing something to help themselves, he used nutritional supplements or tissue salts.

Spoiling a case

Bastyr defined spoiling a case as when a well-indicated remedy does not give results and he found that a case could be spoiled in a number of ways. Foremost, was repeating a remedy too often, especially a nosode. "You will fix the patient so they won't respond to a remedy."

A case could also be spoiled by giving a "third stage remedy" to a patient with a cold, for instance Pulsatilla. Doing so will make the cold extend for over two weeks.

To right a spoiled case, you must start all over. First, wait. During this time, he found he could use electrotherapy, vitamins, and other modalities, but no homeopathic prescriptions.[158]

Coffee and other antidotes

When asked what antidotes the remedies, Bastyr stated, "you can't say for sure."[159] He found that coffee antidoted some remedies, but not all. He advised his patient to decrease coffee because of the health benefits, but did not find that coffee antidoted all remedies."[160] However, if the patient was a heavy coffee drinker, he had different advice. "If the patient is a heavy coffee drinker and you give remedy, the remedy won't start its action." For dietary reasons, he advised his patients to reduce their consumption of coffee. "I tell everyone they should gradually decrease coffee." His advice was to drink only one cup in the morning and to take cayenne pepper for the stimulating effects, instead. [161]

Desensitizing and allergy treatments with Isotherapy

Bastyr used homeopathy to treat allergies and autoimmune disease. He frequently had patients bring in a sample of a substance that they were allergic to and he would potentize it for them. This type of autotherapy was used by Lust. Bastyr claimed it was "not a panacea but effective in sensitive people."[162]

Bastyr potentized substances by using his ultrasound machine to succuss. Remedies were made up in one-ounce bottles. He used this method to remove sensitivity as well as chronic allergies, such as environment or food. In addition, he continued to treat these patients with constitutional homeopathy as well.

Bastyr believed that the remedy worked on some section of

immune system. Possibly the potentized substance's ability to cure was also dependent on immune system.

Patients brought in cats, dog hair, husbands, and dust from their homes; foods, plants from their garden. He found that there were some allergens that would not change. Usually these were cases of constitutional allergies.

Dr. Bastyr used ultrasound to potentize his substances. He diluted to substance to be potentized 1 to 100 using distilled water in a 4-dram vial. Then he placed it on a 10-cm ultrasound head for two minutes to break up the molecular structure. Cam motor swings up an arm with a 4-dram vial on it. Bastyr found this was quicker than potentizing by hand.

Treatment doses were as follows: one drop a day for four days, then increase one drop until they reached a daily dose of 10 drops. After the full ounce bottle was used up, a new bottle of a lower potency was started. The degree of allergic reaction determined the potency. The higher the allergic reaction, the higher to potency. If he started with a 6x potency, the next bottle would be 5x. If the patient had an aggravation reaction at any time, treatment would be suspended for a few days, then reduced by one drop and continued.

Bastyr had one case of a man who was sensitive to poison ivy. Bastyr started him out with 200c, then reduced the potency to 30c, over three months. He waited two weeks between potencies. Eventually he reduced the dose to a 3x and the man was no longer allergic to poison ivy.

Another case was a woman allergic to house dust. He started treating her with a 12x and went up to 10 drops a day after three months. By then, she could do housework with no problem.

Homeopathy and children

Bastyr found that kids like to take homeopathic remedies. Bastyr liked to use homeopathy with children and found it "rewarding because the results are so rapid." [163]He had an occasion where a child ate the whole bottle of a remedy. Dr. Bastyr advised, "Give him a good enema and he'll be alright," adding the warning that sometimes they can have loose stools from lactose.

"We use mostly homeopathy remedies on the kids because they respond so readily; they haven't been drugged to death."

Books

Bastyr enjoined all students to study homeopathy philosophy, particularly the work of James Tyler Kent. "Kent's *Philosophy* and homeopathy books are excellent books to build a framework for natural healing. Basically all natural healing governs on certain results and certain methods of getting well. You must follow these basic skeletal outlines. (Kent) would be a good book to study." [164]

Being an avid reader, Bastyr recalled that the first homeopathic book he read was Nash. He also studied Farrington's *Materia Medica*, which became his favorite book. In his clinic, he frequently consulted Boericke's *Materia Medica*. He frequently referred to Royal's *Textbook of Materia Medica*.[165] He also recommended Allen's book on nosodes, calling it, "An excellent book".[166] He also liked Nash, and regularly used Allen's 12 volume *Encyclopedia* for reference, along with Boericke, but his favorite book was Farrington. "No one can compare to Farrington."[167] He also felt that the British homeopathic journals were "excellent"[168]

Dr. Larkin, from Bellingham, a teacher at Grace Hospital, gave many of his books to Bastyr.

Bastyr noted that Knerr made many valuable additions, and that Bonninghausen contributed the modalities that Bastyr found useful for prescribing: what aggravates and ameliorates. Knerr describes the relationships between remedies and differentials between remedies.

Farrington's comparison of the remedies helped him in differential diagnosis.

Bastyr was also aware that the homeopathic repertories listed times and variations like when moon is on the rise, or full moon, or changes in weather, and felt that these factors played a role in our own nervous system. Some of these factors are no longer noted, but Bastyr felt they were included because, "The old timers were more observant than we are."[169]

Drainage

Bastyr sometimes followed to recommendations of Compton-Burnett, who used nosodes to clear a case before an individual prescription, in order to "jar the amount of toxins that a person has accumulated."[170]

Inimical and concordant remedies

Bastyr learned from E.A. Farrington that certain remedies should not be given close together. Farrington described remedies in families according to their resemblance, and would not mix them. He also used the periodic table describing how one remedy displaced another, especially the metallic remedies. He had been taught that "Metallic remedies act deeper than vegetable remedies."[171] Bastyr took all of this into account in his prescribing.

"Give them powders; don't take them within 20 min. of anything else. Repeat so cycle gets started. Then you can't do too much."

Bastyr felt, "You can antidote with remedies." He looked up the remedy relationships in Boericke's *Materia Medica*, Guernsey, and Knerr's *Repertory*, which lists 50 pages of antidotes. He also used Kent.

He advised, "Don't use things that interfere with the action of the remedy."[172] He kept his remedies separate from the botanical oils and advised, "Don't use any oils around the remedies."[173]

Cell salts

Bastyr also used cell salts therapeutically as well as nutritionally. He used them as intercurrent remedies, while a patient was under constitutional care, and also as placebo, when he did not want to repeat a remedy but wanted to give the patient some remedy to take. He had a broad understanding of the tissue salts, some of it gleaned from Bryant.

He advised that certain cell salts were not to be taken together: for instance, *Kali mur* and *Silica*, or *Silica* and *Mercury*. Some complemented each other, for instance, Calc *sulf*, *Nat sulf* and *Calc phos* work well together, as do *Nat mur* and *Kali phos*. *Calc fluor* and *Kali phos* complement well when used in cardiac conditions.

Because of these remedy relationships, he did not advise the use of the remedy *Bioplasm* as it contains all 12 tissue salts. Bastyr felt "It doesn't work because there are certain inimical salts. You counteract the action."

Calc fluor and *Kali phos* are to be given at night (as is *Nux*).

From a nutritional perspective, he prescribed *Silica* for bone formation, as *Silica* comprises the matrix of the bone, whereas *Nat mur* is a component of the intracellular tissue and *Nat sulf* in the intercellular tissue.

He noted that *Nat sulf* was also a good liver remedy and. found that *Nat mur* was good for treating older people with incontinence. He recommended *Sarsaparilla* is good botanical for treating incontinence as well.

Ferrum phos is useful in congestion, and at the first stage inflammation and also for ecchymose. He called it "the *Arnica* of tissue salts," stating that it could be used instead of *Arnica*. Both *Ferrum phos* and *Kali mur* are useful in acute conditions, *Kali mur* particularly for the second stage of inflammation or when the discharges are light grey.

Kali phos is indicated in long debilitating fevers that don't break, for debility, fatigue, and is also a good hypoglycemic remedy. It corresponds to Pulsatilla because Pulsatilla has both *Kali phos* and *Kali sulf* as part of its chemical makeup. That is the reason for the yellow-green, bland discharge as an indicator for the use of *Pulsatilla*.

The chronic of *Pulsatilla* is *Kali sulf*, whereas the chronic of *Rhus tox* is *Calc fluor.* He found *that Calc fluor* would help absorb bumps on the head in infants, as well as Heberden's nodes in arthritis, varicosities, and hemorrhoids. It is also useful in elastic tissue, venous problem, and for prolapsed uterus. *Calc fluor* aided in back problems as well. Bastyr found that *Calc fluor* could be used when *Rhus tox* failed to act and sometimes it would reactivate the action of *Rhus.*

Conclusion

When I was a first year naturopathic student, eager to learn as much as I could, I approached Dr. B asking for additional study materials. He graciously offered to loan me some books and to talk with me after I finished reading. He loaned me his copy of Hahnemann's *Organon.* I reread the first three paragraphs over and over, amazed, letting the words seep into me, never completely grasping the ideas, overwhelmed by the depth in which I was plunged. After six months, I returned the book, not yet ready to take him up on his offer of discussing it. This book loan began a lifelong trajectory for me. I still strain to comprehend the enormity of Hahnemann's primary vision. In writing this chapter, I marveled that of all the books in Bastyr's library, he chose this one to loan out. I venture to guess that this was not an individualized "prescription," but rather his typical response to students. I never heard him lecture on the *Organon,* but his gesture is louder than words.

Dr. Bastyr used homeopathy every day in his practice. He found that homeopathic remedies brought about quick results. He had a deep understanding and training in both classical and acute prescribing. His joy in homeopathy was spread to generations of students. He carried a link from Hahnemann to the present. He investigated new ideas but kept his focus on the classical and most importantly, the treatments that brought about clinical success using the smallest doses to promote the most "rapid, gentle, permanent restoration of health."[174]

9.
Hydrotherapy

"In hydrotherapy, you will stimulate the body's vitality."

Hydrotherapy was one of the earliest type of therapy. An early textbook on the subject, dating from 1697, was written the British medical pioneer, John Floyer. Kneipp in Germany influenced many in the 1800s. Kneipp utilized both compresses and cold water treatments, but said little about creating healing reactions; however, "in his books you will see he did take them off food, and supplied herbs and minerals."

In the United States in the1900s, the sanitariums of Henry Lindlar and Benedict Lust utilized treatments ranging from water packs to full body wraps and multiple showers. The showers streamed water at different temperatures for 20-30 minutes.

The hygienic movement encouraged fasting and cleaning. The concept involved fasting in order to produce a healing crisis and purify the blood. The patient would be fasted with water while being treated with hydrotherapy in order to produce a healing reaction, causing elimination to take place. Patients were fasted for 7, 14, and 21 days, breaking their fasts on the 8th, 15th, etc.

Hydrotherapy can be used to treat both acute and chronic diseases. Henry Lindlar treated his son, Otto, with water treatment for his meningitis. However, most found that for chronic degenerative diseases, it took time for hydrotherapy to produce the desired healing effects.

Bastyr was a strong believer in hydrotherapy. "Hydrotherapy

with fasting is an area you should not lose; it's a very important modality to have."

Most of the old homeopaths used hydrotherapy with fasting, as well as diet. "They all advised a simple diet, one that was non-toxic diet using foods that were easy to digest, instead of the heavy meats and heavy spicing that was used in those days." Frequently, electrotherapy was included with hydrotherapy treatment, especially to help a patient through a healing crisis.

In his six months studying with O.G. Carroll, Bastyr assisted Carroll in treating 40-50 people a day.[175] He observed patients fasting for up to 42 days but claimed, "I didn't realize how it felt until I took the treatment myself." A patient of Dr Bastyr's who had tic dolorous for two years, was relieved of her symptoms following a 21-day fast.

Before undergoing hydrotherapy, it was advised to build the patient up and to build their vitality in between treatments as well. Carroll would take a urine sample and check for the specific gravity. If it didn't reach 1.5, they would not continue with treatment, as this indicated that the patient's vitality wasn't sufficient to carry him through a healing reaction. The kidney wasn't able to eliminate properly. If kidney function failed, the patient would not survive the fast. If they failed the test, he would build up their vitality before they started hydrotherapy treatment.

Healing crisis

Carroll taught Bastyr that "If they don't continue to produce a healing crisis, the patient won't survive. Don't stop the reaction or you can die."

During a healing crisis, the patient would sometimes develop severe acute symptoms of their original problems: for instance, pneumonia if they had lung problems or jaundice if they had liver problems. Bastyr speculated that the cause of this reaction was in the nervous system, which somehow, "retained the experience" of the original disease.

The whole body was observed during hydrotherapy, watching for signs of healing, healing crisis, and the direction of cure. The urine, the tongue, the pulse, the heartbeat were all observed, as well as temperature and urine. The "old timers" used iridiagnosis, which showed where problems were going to be, which organs were going to be affected.

Changes in the tongue were an early sign of the effect of the therapy. Patients were watched to see in what areas of their tongues would become coated. Circulatory changes were also watched for, either in the extremities, or cerebral, for instance, congestion in head with cold extremities. For example, if there was cerebral congestion, they heated the extremities to equalize the circulation, while placing heat on the feet to decrease cerebral circulation. They used heat to the feet a great deal. If the patient had nausea, a local compress was applied to the feet. "With hydrotherapy, you change your treatment when the patient goes into a reaction."

Some would get delirious during a healing crisis, or develop dilation and pulsing at the celiac axis, or changes in the heartbeat. "Usually the beat will change. First and second sounds. As this changes, you change your hydrotherapy treatment, using either galvanic, short wave, etc., then turn the patient over and use compress on the back."

What follows is an example of the type of treatment used by Carroll. "When they start a reaction, push on the celiac accesses and listens to peristalsis in the gut. Areas in the gut will have no sound — this is when Carroll will use sine wave to start peristalsis, and use herbals also, from laxatives to stimulating herbs, like Gentian, Aloe, Cascara, Senna. And all the water they could handle. He used a rubber stethoscope that he created tension on and listened to the abdomen and heart."

Bastyr continually used hydrotherapy in his practice, though his clinic was not set up with hydrotherapy treatment rooms. He used the philosophy of healing and fasting, as well as the use of packs for varied conditions. He utilized hot and cold water for sitz baths for maternity, and for numerous applications during electrotherapy to increase or decrease circulation to organs or muscle groups. Many mothers were grateful for his hydrotherapy treatment of teething children. (See Treatment Glossary.)[176]

10.
Botanical Medicine

Dr. Bastyr had an extensive and encyclopedic knowledge of botanicals, probably stemming back from his mother and her knowledge of Kneipp. He understood the medicinal usage of plants as well as their chemical makeup, and their chemical functions in the body; for instance, which ones were analgesic, astringents, etc. He often recommended use of a tincture based on the chemical components of the plant; for instance, he would comment on the use of parsley because of its content of apiol. In order to get the desired results when selecting between two liver remedies, he would take into consideration that Chionanthus does more to restore cell function than Chelidonium.

He used herbs in poultices, topically and internally. He would frequently add other treatment modalities to a botanical prescription, for instance, suggesting dietary changes, or adding manipulation, electrotherapy, or vitamins.

As always, his prescriptions were individualized. He was knowledgeable of toxic doses and about what remedies combined with which. And he modified his formulas not just for individual, but for the time in someone's life, taking into consideration their age, temperament, body type, pathology, and sensitivity.

Bastyr made many of the tinctures he used. He and his colleagues ventured to woods and mountains in search of medicinal plants. Some were harvested in his own backyard or garden.

In making tinctures, he used a mixture of 10% glycerin, 30% distilled water, and 60% grain alcohol. "I found that worked about the best for getting extractions."[177]

His knowledge of plants' mineral content led him to harvest plants at different seasons. He claimed that equisetum harvested in the spring contained more calcium mixed with the silica, and preferred a spring harvest for his own use.

He used small dosages, 10 drops in a 1-oz bottle 3-4 times a day.[178] In dispensing tinctures, Bastyr dispensed in 1-oz dropper bottles. "If you give too much at a time, you don't have them (the patient) under your control. You need to see them when you need to see them, to observe them and know their reactions. You never know how sensitive a patient is.""[179] Bastyr was trained by the "Eclectics" who used 5-10 drops in 3-4 oz of water, and used a teaspoon for a dose.

To demonstrate how quickly herbal remedies act, Dr. Bastyr told of a patient who had pleurisy with left sided pain on every breath. He told her to take a mixture of Aconite and Asclepias tuberosa for 24 hours. The patient took 10 drops every hour and went to work the next day. He asked her why she went to work, and she explained that her pain was completely gone.

Dr. Bastyr's usage of botanical medicine has been covered excellently in Dr. William Mitchell's book, *Plant Medicine in Practice: Using the Techniques of John Bastyr*. I gladly refer you to that volume to further elucidate Bastyr's in-depth materia medica and treatment plan. [180]

Therapeutics

Some of his prescriptions are listed in the treatment guide. Below are some further botanical tidbits:

19. Gentian and wormwood. Equal parts, to help formation of hydrochloric acid. A single double O capsule before a meal.

20. Hydrastis works on mucus membranes.

21. He advised using Chionanthus or Taraxacum during
     pregnancy, but not Chelidonium, or Podophyllum.

Books

Below are listed some of the books Bastyr referred to in his clinic
and used in his classes.[181]

King's American Dispensatory, by Harvey Wickes Felter, M.D.,
and John Uri Lloyd, Phr. M., Ph. D., 1898.

American Materia Medica, Therapeutics and Pharmacognosy, by
Finley Ellingwood, M.D., published in 1919.

The Eclectic Materia Medica, Pharmacology and Therapeutics, by
Harvey Wickes Felter, M.D., published in 1922

Modern Herbal, Vols. I and II., Grieve, M. A New York: Dover
Publications, Inc.; 1971

Naturae Medicinae and Naturopathic Dispensatory, Kuts-Cheraux,
A.W., ed. Vol. 3. Eclectic Medical Publications; publishing date
unknown copyright 1953.

11.
Electrotherapy

Electrotherapy treatment stimulates nerves and muscle fibers and organs via pads placed on the body. Electrotherapy devices work in slightly different ways, depending on what type of problem they are treating. Some devices are used to treating pain, while others specialize in muscle stimulation, or reduce or increase circulation to an area of the body.

Dr. Bastyr used electric potencies in his clinic, daily. He employed a variety of electric therapies, often combining them with hydrotherapy, as learned from Dr. Carroll. Short wave and infrared were in frequent use. He also used diathermy, ultrasound, galvanic, damp wave, and even colored light therapy. He had a broad understanding of the types of electricity, how they were generated, as well as what they could be used to treat. About the different electric therapies, Dr. Bastyr said, "They all have their usefulness."[182]

Dr. Bastyr's clinic had an old sine wave machine. The motor generated electricity with cams that could be modulated to increase the flow of the current. Modern versions of this machine had the different currents superimposed.

A frequent treatment was galvanic and sine waves together in treating leg clots of thrombophlebitis. The action of the electric currents caused the clots to reabsorb. He also had success in using galvanic and sine together in the inguinal canal and for varicosities. Typical of his practice, Dr. Bastyr also prescribed the Vitamin C and E for these patients, as he found that treatment with electricity alone was not effective without addressing nutrition.

Galvanic

Galvanic stimulators utilize two elements that react when they are charged with opposite (positive and negative) ions. Studies have shown that galvanic treatment increases local blood flow. It is theorized that edema and toxins can be cleared more readily from an injured area, and the affected tissue will have a greater oxygen supply, thereby retarding infection.[183] Galvanic has been found useful in acute injuries associated with major tissue trauma with bleeding or swelling.

Bastyr treated with galvanic therapy to reduce blood pressure, although, he found the therapy "laborious"[184] because treatments would sometimes take 30-45 minutes. Some patients responded immediately to galvanic treatment, especially if the machine was placed over the liver or kidney. This treatment helped with glomerulas, which were obstructed from calcification, infection, or infiltration.[185]

Ultrasound

Bastyr used ultrasound a great deal. He found it effective for breaking up fibrosis, calcification, and pain in joints. Dr. Bastyr had another creative use for his ultrasound machine. He used it to potentize homeopathic remedies. Rather than succuss by hand, Dr. Bastyr would place a vial on the ultrasound head for 10 minutes. This technique was useful when potentizing substances to treat allergies or a patient's blood in isotherapy. (See Homeopathy Chapter.)

Tens machine

Transcutaneous Electrical Nerve Stimulation or TENS machine was used to frequently used to alleviate pain. The TENS machine works by applying alternating currents.

Diathermy

Diathermy is a high frequency therapy in which electricity is passed through the body between electrodes. Electric current generates heat in the tissues. As the current passes through the body, it has none of the effects of electric currents of lower frequency, because of the resistance offered by the tissues of the body, which may create some form of friction, inducing heat.

This method of heat is different from other heat producing modalities, in that it doesn't raise the temperature of the interior of the body, but just the specific tissues where the electrodes are placed.[186]

Magnatherm

Bastyr found Magnatherm therapy useful because it provided deep heating.[187]

Damp wave

Bastyr's damp wave therapy was an adaptation from E. H. Abrams Damp wave has all the frequencies in it. Damp wave uses a spark gap (which has all the frequencies in it) "By modifying it and running through condensers, you can produce a damp wave, which you can see on an oscilloscope."[188] Bastyr had a damp wave machine in his office that he used until the end of his practice.

Multiple wave oscillator

The electrodes on this machine were arranged in concentric rings, two feet in diameter. This machine would apparently upset television reception for quite a distance. Bastyr reported that, "The FCC would confiscate this one."

Bastyr had a a multi-wave oscillator called an 'Oscilloclast', one of the variety of machines also called "The "Abrams' Box." The Oscilloclast or wave breaker emitted electric waves that were thought to alter or cancel radiation emitted by various diseases.

Dr. Bastyr respected the work of Abrams and studied it extensively, but did not use it in his practice. "I had Abrams' machine and couldn't get the same answer twice.... You can't fool yourself, if you are treating people."

Abrams discovered certain reflexes in the body, which he was able to detect due to his background as a pathologist. Bastyr respected his work, but felt, "His students ruined it."[189] (See Internship and Influences Chapter.)

Radio waves

The spark gap machine also interrupted TV reception in the neighborhood, and the FCC told Bastyr to get rid of it, but he kept one anyway. He found it was the "finest for removing warts, skin growths." He found it excellent for conduction and ease of use. "You can hold one electrode and use your hands to go around the head."[190]

Light therapy

Bastyr used both ultraviolet and infrared therapy in his clinic. He also utilized colored lights. Loeb was one of the influences on Bastyr's colored light therapy. Loeb used carbon arcs with different cores, and projected them through colored prisms. This way he could isolate the colors in the spectrum. Bastyr used the visible spectrum as well; for instance, he commonly utilized cobalt light exposure with for women during pregnancy, in order to prevent hemolytic development of bilirubin in infants. This was also used to treat erythroblastosis.

Oxygen therapy

Another influence on Bastyr was Dr. Schlessie. Schlessie had a machine called Octozone that Dr. Bastyr used in his office. Before that, Schlessie had a unit called a turpazone. It passed air through turpentine with voltage. The high frequency vaporized the turpentine. Treatment with this machine was useful in pulmonary conditions. The problem was that the walls of the clinic room would become coated with gum turpentine.

Schlessie went on to use oxygen and voltage. He believed that created O8, but Bastyr believed it only to be O2 or O3, or ozone. Bastyr used this modality and found it effective in a number of conditions. It was used sometimes in full body exposure, so the entire skin surface would absorb the gases. It was also useful for sinus draining, however the patients had to hold their breath, as the gas was toxic to the lungs, and would cause coughing for 3-4 hours after treatment. The treatment was useful in colitis and for killing pathogens in the colon. Schlessie was known to have injected the gas into hemorrhoids.

Dentistry and electricity

From his understanding of the conduction of electrical currents through metals, Bastyr concluded that any two dissimilar metals would create electric currents in the mouth. He reasoned that two differing metals from a filling could effect the mandibular branch of fifth nerve and have remote effects. A colleague, Dr. Angus Mcfee found he could change someone's bite to produce remission of psoriasis.[191]

Treatment examples

An example of his use of electrotherapy, was a treatment for gall bladder. Bastyr rotated the ultrasound back and forth on the area above the gall bladder, noting that the patient would get nauseous if he didn't keep the ultrasound head moving and the skin would get tender if you stayed in one place too long. Treatment lasted for 10 minutes, followed by a liver massage. "Get a hold of the two sides, and drain it."[192] Bastyr suggested using 3 watts for 10-15 min with a 10-cm head. "If they get achy, cut it down." Treatment was suggested treatment was twice a week, "no oftener or they feel a building fell on them."

For bladder infections, Bastyr used short wave therapy over the bladder.

A sinusitis treatment employed the Magnatherm on a cooling cycle, or infrared, near face until warm then put cold cloth over face and let it warm up.[193]

For enuresis in children, Bastyr used mild sine wave over bladder to stimulate the bladder and sphincter and the third and fourth lumbar.[194]

When he was working on a joint, he used either oil of wintergreen or castor oil for lubrication.

For menstrual cramping he used Magnatherm pulse short wave locally for 20-25 minutes over the pelvis, followed by a cooling cycle.

Bastyr was known to break up everything from migraines to fevers by hooking patients up utilizing the various electrotherapy machines in his practice.

12.

Chiropractic

"Learn to feel with your fingers. You don't go in there and dig with a fork.... Do not pound people, manipulate them."[195]

Dr Bastyr's first licensure was chiropractic. He believed strongly in the power of touch. He passed the chiropractic board exam in 1934, and two years later, took his sanipractic board. When he set up his first office, his office equipment consisted of an adjusting table he made himself. He used traditional manipulation as well as some of the more experimental. For instance he used Stober's technique, now called Nasal Specific. He taught manipulation at National College of Chiropractic. He adjusted nearly all of his patients, and included it in most of his treatment plans.

I hope that someone well versed in his subject will record his work on this subject.

Dr B. had a special technique for adjusting the talus bone in my foot, twisting it with a quick snap. One day in the spring of 1995, I dreamt that Dr Bastyr adjusted my foot. Later that day, I found out he had passed away. Perhaps he traveled to all those he had touched over the years to pass along one final adjustment.[196]

13.
Women's Health

Bastyr treated many of his patients for life. The total health of a woman was taken into consideration, not just her reproductive issues. Because of this, he was able to view her health over generations, following his patients from puberty and childbearing years to menopause and old age, and frequently treating their children as well. He was able to develop valuable clinical understanding, based on his long-term perspective. For instance, he noticed that multiple pregnancies could make a woman susceptible to gall stones and advises his patient likewise, and then checked for gallstones in patients after numerous births. He used a great deal of botanical medicine for women's problems, as well as homeopathy and manipulation.

Fibroids and growths

Bastyr treated many cases of uterine fibroids. He suggested adding essential fatty acids to the diet, and administered electrotherapy in his office – both short wave, and Magnatherm. He was known to dissolve fibroids with homeopathy, using the appropriate remedy for the symptoms.

One remedy frequently used for fibroids was Trillium. Those needing trillium had heavy flow caused by exertion, coughing, lifting, or after standing upright. Bastyr used both tincture (never over

10 drops a day) and 3x potency, but found that the potency was more convenient. Dosage was *Trillium* 3x, four pellets every hour.

In botanical tincture, he used a combination of Trillium with Shepherd's Purse and Geranium, sometimes adding Aletris, or Senecio. Bastyr found that a fibroid that did not bleed would heal. He found that menopause, when the uterus was shrinking, was an ideal time to work on fibroids.

Another case of fibroids was treated with Kali carb 30, given every month. After four months, childhood illness of tonsillitis reoccurred. A few months later, patient returned to her MD Obstetrician and asked him to check her fibroids. He reported that she did not have left-sided fibroids any longer. When the OB was told that they had been dissolved by the use of homeopathy, rather than take her word for it, he palpated again, and told her she had never had fibroids in the first place. "I must have misdiagnosed."[197] .

Bastyr claimed, "We've had remarkable results using homeopathic remedies." In one case he was able to reduce a growth the size of a lemon in four months. Apis and Colocynth were the common remedies. To clear constriction from any tubes he used the homeopathic remedy Dioscorea. He also had curative results using homeopathic remedies for enlarged or cystic ovaries.

Bastyr treated many breast cancers that "disappeared." One of his treatments was topical application of the remedy *Cundurango* in 3x potency.

Vaginal packs

Bastyr used numerous types of vaginal packs for healing. Packs were utilized to treat inflammation, cervicitis, and effects of gonorrhea, scarring, and fibroids. He had cases of Class 5 PAP smears reduce to Class 1 with treatment. For this, he used vaginal packs as well as homeopathic remedies: *Magnesium phos, Colocynth* and *Vibernum* (which was also used to treat dysmenorrhea).

For pain relief, Bastyr frequently relied on his expertise in manipulation. A typical adjustment for menses pain was pressure over exit of lumbar nerve at third lumbar for one to three minutes with thumbs. He was also known to use Magnatherm for 20-25 minutes over the pelvis followed with a cooling cycle.

Homeopathy for women

Bastyr utilized a great deal of homeopathy in treating women's health issues. He referred to the homeopathic remedy, *Lachesis* as "a very fine female remedy." He found it to be useful for dysmenorrhea and the hot flashes of menopause (see Treatment Guide). *Lachesis* was also indicated for problems in the left ovaries or for a history of left-sided ovarian problems that moved to the right.

14.
Pregnancy and Childbirth

Pregnancy

Dr. Bastyr joked that he was "very good at getting women pregnant."[198] He had patients as far away as Washington DC and Virginia who sought him out for fertility. His treatment included herbal, nutrition, manipulation, and homeopathy. He also counseled lifestyle changes when needed.

Constitutional homeopathy was used to help with fertility, as well as miasmatic theory. Dr. Bastyr said that "the old timers" believed that infertility stemmed from a psoric background and they used *Tuberculinum* to clear it, as well as other psoric remedies.

In treating infertility, his casetaking was extensive, as always. He exhausted every avenue, from the structural, to nutritional, constitutional, miasmatic.[199] "You must get the history. You must get the background, so you know what the patient is going to have to go through." He thoroughly investigated and blockages caused by structural problems such as blocked tubes. The husband was also tested for sperm mobility and viability. He used hair analysis and blood work to support any dietary recommendations.

If there was a history of infections or pelvic inflammatory disease, that had to be corrected as well. Bastyr used electric therapy to treat pelvic inflammatory symptoms as well as homeopathy and manipulation.

Dr. Bastyr recommended sitz baths for all his pregnant women.

(See Treatment Glossary.) Sitz baths were also recommended to increase fertility, when taken a few days before and after ovulation.

In cases with a history of stillbirth, or midterm abortions, Bastyr took the case of both parents prior to conception. When asked if natural methods could prevent possible hereditary conditions, Bastyr replied, emphatically, "Yes."[200]

Natural Delivery

Bastyr delivered hundreds of babies. He did underwater births and home births. Babies delivered at home were put in a warm ovens or wood stoves to keep warm. He charged 50 cents a visit for prenatal care and saw his patients every two weeks, then every week for last six weeks. At one time he had two nurses assisting him. When he had two deliveries at the same time, he'd send a nurse out first. Bastyr sometimes traveled great distances and through inclement weather to deliveries. He once delivered a breach baby on Mount Si at 2,500 feet during a snowstorm. He could only drive up to about 1000 feet, so he got out and walked the rest of the way with all of his equipment in an OB bag. The baby was delivered and was fine.[201]

Training the mothers-to-be

Dr. Bastyr educated each of his pregnant patients on the mechanisms of labor. He described each stage of labor so they'd know what was happening and know what to expect. Since he had no models, he showed them anatomical photos and demonstrated with a tube and an eraser.

He used hypnosis and his gentle demeanor to advise them to consider contractions as expulsive effort and not as pain

In his deliveries, he used very little anesthesia and nitrous oxide very seldom. He also used hypnosis to induce relaxation.

He was able to stimulate labor with herbs and homeopathics, for instance Caulophylum 10-15 drop doses. "If you are going to do OB, keep your remedies around and they'll save you lots of trouble."[202]

Bastyr believed in changing dietary habits when needed. All of his patients were advised on diet and lifestyle. He advised mothers-to-be to consume no salt and to eat two or three raw carrots a day. Exercises were recommended for the abdominal muscles and the back, as well as breathing exercises. Squats and deep knee bends were advised, in order to increase perineal elasticity.

Bastyr had an herbal formula he called Mother's Cordial, containing Vibernum, Aletris and Mitchella. Caulophylum was added in the last six weeks Patients also took sitz baths and prepared for breastfeeding with applications of olive oil and lemon juice.

Bastyr used light therapy with his pregnant patients. He exposed them to cobalt blue light, finding that the exposure reduced stretch marks and soreness. Those who had this treatment had less painful contractions and shorter labor time.

Turning a baby

Bastyr didn't have many breach babies because he turned them in utero. He used manipulations and homeopathy to ensure the baby would stay turned. Both Pulsatilla and Gelsemium were utilized turn babies, though he counseled not to give Pulsatilla too early as it could start labor. Using homeopathy after the inversion ensured that the baby would stay turned.

Water births

Bastyr did quite a number under water deliveries. He found that using the tub shortened labor time. When the patient was dilated two to three fingers (he used finger not centimeter measurements), or had steady contractions (1-2 minutes, 5 min apart) they'd put them in the tub. The bathtub was cleaned beforehand using Lysol and Epsom salts were added to the warm water. Patient was submerged up to her head with a towel covering her abdomen. The water was kept in motion to promote contractions. As crowning took place, Bastyr would remove the mother to a delivery table or allowed the baby to be born in the water, as the baby wouldn't breathe under water, and would yell when they got to the surface. "Bathtub babies are easy."[203]

Bastyr found it easier to deliver on a table if there was a prolonged labor with no progress. He used no stirrups, but tied the patient's feet to boards. Bastyr counseled to always deliver the baby lying on its right side so the blood would flow from the baby's heart — right ventricle to left. He explained that "a flap goes over and closes if you put them on left."

Botanicals

As in all of his practice, Bastyr used many botanical remedies, both in tincture and homeopathic potency, but found that some were counter-indicated during pregnancy. He used Chionanthus and Taraxacum for patients during pregnancy, but not Chelidonium, or Podophyllum.[204]

Nursing

Bastyr advised his patients to nurse if at all possible. Bastyr was watchful of a nursing mother's diet, suggesting avoiding foods that could case colic, or adding foods to increase milk production.
For nursing mothers, Bastyr noted that taking thyroxin free thyroid helped with milk production, and also suggested eating carrots and the addition of iodine in the diet. Barley could also be used to stimulate milk production, along with the botanical, Blessed Thistle. He advised drinking peppermint tea or using peppermint oil, as it was not known to cause problems to nursing infants.[205]

15.

Treatment of Children

Dr. Bastyr was a true family doctor. He treated families for decades, ensuring that the health of each following generation was improved. He cared for pregnant mothers before they conceived, and treated the children he delivered for four months after their birth, and sometimes for a lifetime. Because of his close presence in the lives of the children in his care, he was able to exact deep changes in the constitution not only of individual, but of families as well.

He enjoyed working with children. "Treating youngsters is very rewarding because results are very rapid."

Treatment during first four months of life

Bastyr treated the babies he delivered for four months post partum. He advised parents against childhood vaccinations and provided Homeoprophylaxis instead. (See Homeopathy Chapter.)

"I never had a polio case develop in a youngster we delivered. We used *Lathyrus*... Dr. Grimmer in Illinois claimed that the Opsonic Index was increased by the use of *Lathyrus* in polio prevention...We gave it to youngsters in summer time, the time of prevalence of polio." Treatment consisted of "eight little pellets of 30c" to take once a week.

He also understood the need for proper nutrition in building a healthy constitution. "If you keep your family in a nutritious state, their immune system can be built." For bottle fed babies, Bastyr ensured that they were given Lactobacillus bifidus as a nutritional supplement.

Diagnosis

When examining a child, Bastyr was thorough. He observed the shape of head, chest, mouth, jaw, arch of the mouth, spacing of eyes, condition of the fontanels. He looked at small details as well, for instance the color of tissues, or dryness. He did not hesitate to put his finger in a child's mouth. "If you can get your hand in there, let him bite your hand a couple of times and you can find out what it's like in there."

He used percussion to check the size of internal organs. "Percussion is very informative if you take your time." He checked the spleen, liver, and thymus, checked musculature that might someday give way to hernia and provided preventative treatment if he detected any developmental tendencies.

He worked patiently, often having the mother hold the child until it trusted him.

He used the same thorough techniques for children as for adults, consulting testing whenever necessary, however he found that children's vitality provided an added dimension to conventional diagnostics. He jokingly admitted, "We used to do cultures but by the time the culture came back, the kid was well."

His diagnosis included observation, touch, palpation, taking a family history and any labs tests necessary, as well as listening. "Always listen to the child when he cries." A hoarse cry can indicate pneumonia, for example.

Treatments

Typical of his multiple modality approach, Bastyr had remedies for enuresis ranging from herbal, to homeopathic, to electrical, to chiropractic, suggesting sine wave over the bladder, or manipulating the lumbar. He used hot and cold sitz baths to tone the pelvis and advised exercises for bladder retention. He also checked the urine with lab tests, along with teaching the mother how to give hypnotic suggestions to the child before sleep, suggesting that when bladder gets full they will feel it and wake up and go to bathroom.

If he found a predisposition to hernia in a child, he prescribed *Lycopodium* 30c once a month this would cause the hernia to grow over. He saw that happen many times in his practice. He was able to follow patients he had as children for 20 years to see that no hernia developed in the ones treated in this manner.

Cell salts were commonly utilized in treating otitis media. He recommended Kali mur 6x, with frequent repetition. If the children would not take the tablets, he had the parents dissolve 12 pellets in an ounce of water and give a teaspoon every hour claiming, "This is how old timers used to used it. This will pull the fluid out of the ear," and was considered to be a specific for eustachian catarrhal conditions.

He used the tissue salt of Natrum phos for lymphatic tissue as well as for the ill effects of inoculations, (along with Silica and Thuja). For colic, he advised just a drop of Magnesium phosphoricum 3x or 6c or homeopathic Dioscorea.

He had many diarrhea remedies. Tied to typology, he would use *Calcarea phos* for a thin baby with slow to close fontanels, whose stool was watery and gaseous. If the mother had eaten excess protein prior to a baby's diarrhea, especially fish, he suggested homeopathic *Arsensicum*. He recommended slippery elm or barley gruel to stop irritation in a nursing baby. His mentor, Dr. Peters taught him to prescribe toasted rye flour in a teaspoon with water to stop diarrhea. A mixture of equal parts of sauerkraut and tomato juice could be used to replace fluids and electrolytes.

For enlarged tonsils, Bastyr looked to the background of the family, and commonly prescribed nosodes. (See Homeopathy Chapter.)

In treating children with skin problems he commonly found a history of allergies in the family. In these cases he would find out what the allergies were and neutralize them. (See Treatment Glossary.)

Hydrotherapy

Bastyr frequently used hydrotherapy with children. For fever, he frequently utilized heat to the feet and compresses to the chest, to remove congestion from the chest. For diarrhea, he used cold compresses on the child's abdomen with heat to the feet, especially if there was cramping as well. He advised the use of cold wet socks to soothe teething children. (See Treatment Glossary), along with homeopathic doses of *Chamomilla* 3x to 30c.

Bastyr taught parents how to bathe their children, suggesting they not be taken out of a warm bath while their blood vessels were still dilated. He advised cooling the child down first, in order to assist the development of immunity to the seasonal changes in temperature. This same treatment was advised for children who came down with frequent colds. After bathing, parents were to finish with a cold rub, starting with extremities, then adding the whole body. This, he said, would stimulate the immune system. "Teach them to do that and the child will become more or less immune, especially to changes in temperature." He explained that, "The skin is the largest proprioceptive organ we have. Stimulation from inside can go outside to the various organs and nervous system."

Homeopathy

Bastyr frequently prescribed homeopathic remedies for treating children. "We use mostly homeopathy remedies on the kids because they respond so readily; they haven't been drugged to death."

When addressing a medical problem, he treated the cause, not only the symptoms. He used specific treatments for otitis media, but also looked at the background state of the child. "If you get kids with their tubes in ears and recurring ears infections, glands are involved, and enlarged tonsils or adenoids. We always use nosodes, either *Bacillinum* or *Tuberculinum*, one dose a month of 30c or 200c, until lymphadenopathy goes down."

Typology

Using constitutional homeopathy as a guide, Bastyr identified children's remedies by what is now called keynote prescribing. He used pictures of the totality of the remedy to help him identify the correct remedy. For instance, he noted that *Sulphur* children are itchy and have bright red lips or red around any orifice: eyes, nose, anus, almost vermilion.

The *Calcarea carbonicum* youngster is prone to cradle cap. This is the remedy for those children with abdominal bloating and night sweats, or a restless child who throws the covers off at night. They tend to be pale and flabby.

The Graphites child is obese and exhibits cracks behind his ears, eyes that agglutinate at night, and indigestion.[206]

16.
Suggestions to Research

1. Bastyr repeated told his students there was "a lot of work to be done." Here are some of his suggestions for further research.

2. How does meditation affect the different organs of the body?[207]

3. E. H. Minz classified the different organs and their origins according to the layers of embryonic origin. Bastyr advised his students that this was "an idea you might look into."[208]

4. Why are certain remedies best given at night? *Calc fluor* and *Kali phos* are to be given at night. Just like *Nux* is best given in the evening. "Don't know why; it's up to you fellows to tell me so."

5. Some plants have action of absorption of fatty acids. Like gammalinolaic acid and effect of action of prostaglandin, deposition on cell walls. Do research to determine if they act on intercellular, intracellular, or on nerve supplies to muscles of heart, or muscles of blood vessels.[209]

6. How do homeopathic remedies act? Bastyr felt that the action was due to changes produced in the immune system. "Formation and release in receptor sites of lymph cells that change it so body can recognize invaders. This is where

answers will come. If we had electron microscope so you can see change in intracellular structure. This is where we are going to go."[210]

7. How do you account for action of 6x homeopathic remedy acting for two years? [211]

8. Electrotherapy – I hope some will go into research on electrotherapy, some into teaching.[212]

9. "Your class should do a proving. That's one way you can learn to get the essence of a remedy."[213]

THERAPUETICS

17.
Bastyr's Clinical Homeopathic Materia Medica

Aconite
First stage of a cold. Also for earaches.
Use for angina, with numbness and tingling of fingers and arms.
General formula (syrup): *Aconite, Sclastris secundrum, Phytolacca, Hydrastis.* (From Dr. Eli Jones.)

Allium sativa
For a cold that goes to the chest.

Allium cepa
For a cold with watery eyes and irritated nose.
Head colds that stay in the head.

Alloxan
For diabetes use 12x. (DD *Phlorizinum, Phos acid.)*

Aloe
Ulcerative colitis with frequent stool, excessive mucus, involuntary mucus when passing gas.
Wake at night with involuntary stool. Use 200c

Apis
Meningitis following small pox vaccination. And effusions.

Apocynum
Diabetes. Use12x.

Arbutin
For bladder inflammation.

Arnica
Tooth extractions — use *Arnica* and *Hypericum* every two hours before and after for no bruising.
Useful in deliveries to prevent bruising.

Arsenicum
Used to prevent Montezuma's revenge in travelers.
For diarrhea in children with irritation around anus following stool. Especially if mother ate excess protein prior to baby's diarrhea, especially fish.
Burning with diarrhea and craving small quantities of warm water to drink.

Ars iodatum
Bronchitis. Use 2x.
Sinus infection when burning runs down the nose and raw area on upper lip.
Psoriasis. Shedding skin "like snow on the floor."

Artium lappa
For ADHD kids with skin problems.

Arum trifillum
Sinus infection with watery discharge, raw red nose, constantly wiping it.
Mucus: clear to yellow alternate or bleeding.

Bacillinum
Well-indicated for mononucleosis when there is adenopathy.

Belladonna

For early strep throat, use 3x, 6x. (Combine with *Phytolacca*).
Indicated with high BP, fever, throbbing pulse with cold hands and feet.
To increase circulation to the extremities and decrease cerebral congestion. (Also use hydrotherapy for this purpose.)
Sweat on uncovered parts, doesn't like head low. Likes to sit up instead.
Delirium.
First stage of meningitis. Hallucinations, congestion without effusions.
Counter indicated in glaucoma because it can increase intraocular pressure.
Earaches. Use 3x 6x.
Belladonna for sphincter spasm that causes enuresis in children.
Main remedy for mumps. (DD *Rhus tox.*)

Berberis aquafolia

ADHD kids.
Combine *Berberis, Echinacea, Thuja, Chamomilla* for cystitis with pus and irritation.

Bryonia

Good for Joints, lungs, head.
This is the remedy that Lippe gave Bryant's wife to cure her ankle.
Bursitis. Frozen shoulder.
Sharp piercing pain.
Bryonia for rt. sided pleurisy. If lying and holding relieve pain, pain with every inspiration. Knife-like shooting pains. One dose of tincture. Pale swollen ankles (not red). Skin looks tight, like it's going to break.
Good liver remedy. Irritability. Patient resents being questioned, answers curtly.
For fever with effusion.
Breast infections.

Cactus

In any coronary involvement.

Will relieve angina.

Symptom of tightness like a band. Frequent doses 5-10 drops in 1/2-hour time. Especially if there is a feeling of compression. If it's gone so far that MI has developed, remedy won't work. Otherwise, you can help coronaries with *Cactus*.

Calcarea carb

Youngster with cradle cap, especially if bloated tummy and night sweats.

Or restless kid who throws off covers at night. Have big belly. Pale child, flabby, white.

Cough comes on at 3 am. Terrible weakness. Cough and exhausted. They raise yellow mucus. (DD *Stannum*.)

Calc fluor

Good for scars.

For cataracts. Use 200c 1-2 doses

Ankylosis.

Chronic of *Rhus tox*. Good for a "crick in back."

Calc sulf

Boils, where there is extra bleeding. The boils are open and draining. (DD *Hepar sulf*)

Cineria maritima (Senecio)

For cataracts – apply liquid locally.

Cantharis

Useful for Lupus cases.

Capsicum

Use with *Cantharis* (Bay rum) to grow hair.

Also recommended as a coffee substitute for those who want a coffee buzz.

Causticum
Remedy for cracking joints.
Enuresis. For children who urinate first thing at night.

Caulophylum
Pain whole pelvic pain and radiating down thighs. Use in potency or tincture.
A good remedy to stimulate labor. Use 10-15 drops and repeat up to 3-4 times.

Chamomilla
Earaches.
Colic.
Teething remedy. Use *Chamomile* 3x.

China arsenicosum
Hypertension.

Colocynth
For ovarian cysts use 30c twice a day.
Pelvic pain relieved by pressure and heat.
Colic, if a child pulls his knees up with the pain.

Cocculus
For sea sickness.

Chelidonium
Good for inflammations.
Liver and gall stone remedy.

Chionanthus
Gallstone remedy, can be used during pregnancy.

Convallaria
Good for long term use in heart problems. Combine with *Crataegus*. Indicated if they can't breathe if they lie down.

Crataegus oxyacantha
Heart problems – mix with cactus, equal parts for any coronary involvement. Use lower potencies.

Croton tiglium
Diarrhea that occurs rapidly after eating.

Cundurango
Apply topically for tumors of the breast. Use 3x.

Cuprum
Spasmodic choking cough, dry cough.

Digitalis
Intermittent pulse, worse exertion, or with dyspnea and cyanosis. Use 3x to 6x.
Calcium potentiates the action of *Digitalis*.

Dioscoria
Intestinal spasms. (Also *Lobelia*.)
For any tubular structures – causing relaxing of spasm or constriction.
Colic – if a child extends his body, with the pain.
Aids passage of gall stones.

Equisitum
For bladder problems.

Euphrasia
For conjunctivitis. Use 12x every 15-min then every hour after.
Cataracts.

For colds with burning eyes and bland nose discharge.

Fluoric acid
Good for scars. Hemangeomas also.
Osteo deposits.

Gelsemium
Good remedy for ADHD.
To turn a baby in utero. (See *Puls.*)

Graphites
Obese child who cracks behind ears, oozing. Eyes agglutinate at night.
Also have indigestion.

Hepar sulf
Boils. *Hepar* will open boil, but has to have multiple heads on it. Use *Calc sulf* if there is a little extra bleeding. *Calc sulf* has boils that are open and draining.

Hydrangea
Cystitis with crystals.

Hyoscyamus
Enuresis with bladder distension.

Hydrocotyle asiatica
For treating lupus. Use 3x. "One of my good remedies for lupus."

Indigo
Epilepsy – 6x. Take 3 every 6 hours.

Isotherapy
To desensitize allergen Use patient's blood or urine. Potentize up to 30c. Give 1-drop doses and increase drops every four days.

Kali carb
Right sided shooting pains.
They have to sit up to cough, lean forward.

Kali mur
For earaches in children, use 6x, and repeat often. Dissolve 12 tablets in an ounce of water, and give a teaspoon every hour to pull the fluid out of the ear.

Ipecac
Red colored sputum.
Vomit or gag with cough.

Lachesis
Lupus. (Agg sun, constriction. Can't stand tight clothes. Agg night.)
Dysmenhorea relieved by flow. If flow is dark, not bright red, *Lach* will work.
Hot flashes. Use 8x daily or once a week.
Left sided ovarian problems, especially if they then move to the right.

Lathyrus sativa
Use for preventative for polio.

Lemna minor
For sinus infection from damp and rain.

Leptonania
(See *Lomatium dissectum.*)

Lomatium dissectum
For influenza or pneumonia. This remedy was used during the influenza epidemic in the Great Basin area in the 1920's. The appearance of a rash is a sign to lower the dose.
Also for kidney problems following infection.

Lycopodium
To prevent hernia in children with an abdominal defect. Use 30c.
Never below 30. Higher OK. Give once a month.
Lycopodium antidotes digestive problems after antibiotics.

Lycopus
For hyperthyroid 10 drops QID.

Mag phos
Cramps relieved by heat and pressure.
For children add a drop of 3x 6x in a spoon of hot water for colic or
intestinal spasms.

Medhorrinum
Sleep with butt in air. Only one remedy has this symptom.
Chronic cases of cystitis.

Mercury dolsis
Use 12c for worms.

Natrum phos
As a tissue salts, use for lymphatics.
Also ill effects of inoculations.

Natrum sulf
Very effective in head injuries whether due to edema in the mem-
brane that swell after head injuries.
Also a good flu remedy.
Basal ganglia remedy.
Useful for a "hydrogenoid constitution" that can't stand wet damp.
Nat sulf is a great liver remedy.
Diabetes remedy. Use 3c to 10M. *Nat sulf* will pull out a lot of fluids
from diabetic's tissues that are floppy and watery.

Nitric acid
Cystitis. Use12x-30x.

Nux vomica
(See *Phytolacca.*)
For a cough when a warm hand becomes cold.
Spinal cord irritation.
Also for lockjaw 200c.

Parabenzoquinon
Via injections (6x) for cancer and leukemia. (See Dr. Coke, Internship Chapter.)

Phlorizinum
For diabetes use 6x. (DD *Phos acid, Alloxan.*)

Polygonum aviculare
For atherosclerosis, use 10 drops of tincture a day.
Also useful in preventing and removing kidney stones.

Polymnia uvedalia
A spleen remedy.

Phosphoric acid
Remedy for diabetes. Use 6x to 30c (DD *Phlorizinum, Alloxan.*)

Phytolacca
For solid tumors in the breast.
To treat hypothyroid, combine tinctures of *Phytolacca, Viscum album,* and small amounts of *Nux vomica,* each in 1x to 6x tincture. Use whole plant and berries for tincture. Take daily.
For sore throat with pain in ear when swallow.

Pulsatilla
To turn a baby in utero (*Gelsemium* too). Don't give *Pulsatilla* too

early as it can start labor but use after the inversion to make sure the baby stays turned.

Rhus tox
Can be used to remove allergy to poison ivy. Start with 200c, once a month. Then go to 30c, 12c, 6c, 3c. If the patient reacts, go back up to a higher potency and stay with that potency until the symptom decrease.
Arthralgias In acute cases. With soreness, stiffness in morning, frequent doses low potencies, then run potency up. If there are rashes start high and come down.
If rash is typical, vesicular, use it high then come down.
Main remedy for mumps. (DD *Belladonna*)

Rumex
Cough with tickle in supersternal fossa. Cough when breathing, cough when lying down. Cough when talk, laugh.

Ruta
For any sprain, or tennis elbow.
For eye strain.
Use 30c.

Sabina
Pain during menses that radiates to the back.
For pain across sacrum during childbirth.

Scirrhinum
To treat breast cancer.

Serum angular
Repeated doses reduce proteinurea. 3x – 6x.

Silica
Ill effects of vaccination

Spongia tosta
Thyroid remedy, especially if thyroid is swollen and there is a feeling of choking. Use 3x.
Bronchial cough. Useful if they cough and choke at the same time, or make a sawing noise. Can't breathe when there is something in front of their faces. Cough worse after exertion.

Spigelia
For removing worms.

Sulphur
Itchy kids with bright red lips or red around any orifice, eyes, nose, anus, almost a vermilion.

Staphysagria
Remedy for poor teeth. (DD *Mercury*.)

Sticta pulmonaria
Sinus inflammation with painful dryness and sneezing.

Stramonium
Enuresis from urine retention.

Strychnine phos
Hypertension.

Symphytum
Sprain or bruise from crushing blow.

Syzygium jambolanum
For diabetes – use as a tea combined with huckleberry leaves and Siranda blanca.

Tabacum
For sea sickness.

Thiosinamine

Scars or keyloids. Some of the "old doctors"(Mackenzie) injected *Thiosinamine* into scar tissue to break it up, but Bastyr believed in never breaking the skin.

Thuja

Ill effects of vaccination.

Thryroidinum

To treat hyperthyroid, use 200c.

Tuberculinum

Night sweats.
Infertility.

Veratrum veride

Hypertension- Use 6x. Never use in tincture.
Useful in fever with high congestion. Acts rapidly.
Good remedy for acute congestion. Congestive phase.
Pneumonia where the pulse in increased, redness. If the pulse rate goes below 60 (if you are using tincture), dose is toxic.
Useful in hypertension (along with *Viscum album* and *Allium sativa.* (see Therapies.)
For diarrhea with severe cramps prior to discharge and cold sweats.
Do not use below 30c.

Vibernum

For dysmenorhea.

Viscum album

(See *Phytolacca.*)
Useful in heart problems, can be combined with *Veratrum* and *Allium sativa*. Works on vascular tissues, not heart itself.
Tic dolorous – one drop a day (tincture).

Xinc valerianate
For ADHD.

Zanthoxylum
Use for diarrhea.

18.
Treatment Guide

Adrenal
Add manganese and zinc.

ADHD children
Herbals: Valerian. Burdock.
Homeopathic: *Gelsemium, Xinc valerianate. Artium lappa* for ADHD kids with skin problems.

Angina
Cactus in any coronary involvement with symptom of tightness like a band. Frequent doses 5-10 drops in 1/2-hour time. Especially if compression feeling. If it's gone so far that MI has developed, remedy won't work. Otherwise, you can help coronaries with cactus.

Antibiotics, ill effects of
Lycopodium antidotes digestive problems after antibiotics.

Antispasmodic formula
Skunk cabbage, lobelia, and capsicum. "Equal parts would wake a dead man. Give a 1/2 teaspoon (or 15 drops in water) and follow with chases of cold water and he'll rise up off the floor."[214]

Appendicitis
Turpentine (Terebinthinum) hot turpentine compresses on flannel. Place pack on abdomen.

Arthralgias
Use *Rhus tox.* In acute cases. With soreness, stiffness in morning, frequent doses low potencies, then run potency up. If there are rashes start high and come down.

Use *Rhus tox* in typical symptom, agg cold, and relief motion. If they have rashes, if skin is involved, don't give them *Rhus* to begin with. As they progress with vascular problems. If rash is typical, use it high then come down.

Arthritis
"Formula A." Mix equal parts Yucca, Devil's claw, Chaparral, and half portions of Cimicifuga and Alfalfa. Take two OO caps or a half-teaspoon QID, with very hot water. Cut to three times a day, as pain gets better. In 6-8 weeks there should be some relief. This won't reduce deposits, but will take swelling out. Best to use long term.

Atherosclerosis
Polygonum aviculare 10 drops of tincture a day. Also useful in removing kidney stones.

Bastyr's Formula
Used to treat intestinal pain and inflammation, Crohn's disease, ulcerative colitis and other inflammatory bowel diseases.
Ingredients: Althea officinalis, Echinacea angustifolia, Ulmus fulva, Geranium maculatum, Phytolacca, Hydrastis canadensis, Cabbage powder, Baptisia tincture, Pancreatine, Duodenal substance, niacinamide

Breast cancer
Make a syrup of tinctures of Hydrastis, Phytolacca, Salistra secundrus, cordalis. Mix the first three in equal parts and other in quarters.

Take teaspoon four times a day.
Apply *Cundurango* 3x for tumors.

Bronchitis
Ars iodatum 2x.

Bursitis
Use 1-drop doses of *Bryonia* tincture or low potency homeopathic. Repeat every two hours.
Also use ultrasound and manipulation. Use galvanism 2% Procaine. For 8-15 minutes. Negative pad to shoulder.

Boils
Hepar sulf or *Calc sulf*. *Hepar* will open a boil, but has to have multiple heads on it for *Hepar* to be useful. Use *Calc sulf* if there is a little extra bleeding. A boil needing *Calc* sulf is always open and draining.

Mercury poisoning
Can use homeopathic *Mercury*. Or *Selenium*.
Glandulars: take spleen, lymphatic, to counteract effects of mercury in mouth. Should reduce in 3-6 months.

Mother's cordial
Use before delivery: Mitchella repens, Caulophylum, Thelonius.

Carpal tunnel
Use sound wave on it and "our good friend" castor oil.
Castor oil is always good to use topically and internally.

Cataracts
Calc fluor 200c, 1-2 doses.
Cineria maritima (Senecio). Liquid – apply locally.
Euphrasia.
Lemon in eye. Honey. Flax seed itself. Drop in eye. Tears will get

out oil, which will lubricate the eye.

Colds

Aconite tincture in very small doses or 3x potency. *Aconite* is useful until perspiration occurs. At that time, *Aconite* has accomplished all it can do. Tincture is 1/10 drop in 1 oz. For first congestive stages, with a fever, hot, restless. If there is tingling or numbness (on tongue or extremities), too much is used.

Colic /Intestinal spasm

Mag phos – a drop of 3x 6x in a spoon of hot water.
Colocynthis-if a child pulls his knees up with the spasms.
Dioscoria – if a child extends with the pain.

Crohn's disease

Raw pig intestinal mucus.
6.000-10,000 unit doses of Vit. E.

Colitis – chronic ulcerative

(See Crohn's disease.)

Compresses

Always cover compresses with wool, seal them in, especially cold compresses.

Conjunctivitis

Use Hydrastis eye drops.
Chlorophyll.
Pink eye. *Euphrasia* 12x every 15 min then every hour after. *Euphrasia* is homeospecific for conjunctivitis.

Constipation

Give Cascara sagrada extract 15 drops three times a day until bowels move. Decrease by one drop a day until five drops. Hold there for 4-6 weeks, the decrease to 1-2 drops for 4-6 weeks.

Hydrotherapy enema. Use amount water needed to bowels started. Add to the water lactic acid or lemon juice or molasses, buttermilk, or yogurt. Use amount needed for relief. After emptying, follow with 8 oz of plain cold water enema. Each time, gradually decrease amount of water in first enema. Finish with cold after they've emptied, until you only use the cold 8-oz. Then decrease the amount of cold water. Can be used in conjunction with Cascara.
Sine wave can be used to increase circulation.

Cough syrup
Leptania and Asclepias tuberosa in tincture. Can add Lobelia.

Cradle cap
Add magnesium to diet.
Possible *Calc carb* child constitutionally.

Cystitis
Sitz baths.
Nitric acid 12-30x.
Cystitis with pus and irritation: *Berberis, Echinacea, Thuja, Chamomilla*
Cystitis with strangury: *Urva ursi, Althea, Juniper berries*
Cystitis with crystals: *Hydrangea*

Cystic breast
Recommended ultrasound over mammogram.
Glyceriza in gel form with Phytolacca.
For a cyst, use Vit E and *Nat phos* internally and *Phytolacca* internally.
Burning and sensitive with itching or stinging is *Apis*, for rt. or left.
For a solid tumor, use *Phytolacca*.
Oil can be used hot compress until breast pink. Massage in oil, then apply cold compress and leave on covered with wool to dry oil in.
Also must give patient thymus and a general preventive diet.
Get them off coffee and salt and sugar. All three.
If they are sensitive to any foods get them off that too.

Diabetes

Phosphoric acid. Good remedy for diabetes 6x to 30c.

Nat sulf use from 3c to 10M. *Nat sulf* will pull out a lot of fluids. Diabetic tissues are floppy and watery. Not normal tissue tone.

Diabetes (Cont.)

Put them on strict diet, low carb, and some complex carbs. Frequent eating, six times a day, with reduced wheat and sugar. Large doses of raw liver several times a day. Add minerals, chromium, Mag, Vit C, A, B6, zinc.

Herbal teas. Combine Syzygium jambolanum (jumbol seeds) huckleberry leaves. Siranda blanca.

Take them off coffee. Coffee is bad for diabetics.

Homeopathically, use *Alloxan* 12x. Or *Phlorizinum* 6x.

Diarrhea

If occurs rapidly after eating, *Croton tiglium.*

In children if diarrhea occurs with *irritation* around anus following stool use *Arsenicum.* Especially if mother ate excess protein prior to baby's diarrhea, especially fish.

Use barley gruel to stop irritation in nursing babies, or slippery elm. Or Amaranth. Or toasted rye flour. Give a teaspoon with water every half-hour.

Sauerkraut and tomato juice, tablespoon of each. Every 20 minutes for 24 hours. Or juice raw cabbage juice or raw potato.

Barley apple pectin. Chew apple well. Don't eat skin.

Homeopathy: Use *Arsenicum alb* 6, 12, for diarrhea with burning and craving small quantities of warm water.

Veratrum ver. as severe cramps prior to discharge and cold sweats. Do not use below 30c.

Cold compress or with nausea, give them Zanthoxylum. Prickly ash berries.

Botanical: tinctures of Lobelia. Echinacea and Baptisia. (Equal parts) you can add Hydrastis. This will heal the gut.

Use Robert's Formula.

Dysmenorrhea

Use hot mustard footbaths for 15 min, as hot as you can bear it. Put cold compress on abdomen below navel and leave foot in bath for 15 more minutes, then remove feet and keep cold on abdomen for 30 more minutes.

Earaches

Belladonna, Aconite, Chamomilla. 3x to 6x.

Electrolyte replacement

Mix half sauerkraut juice and half tomato juice and sip as needed, also tsp. of cabbage juice can be used for children.

Enuresis (in children)

First thing at night, *Causticum. Belladonna* if caused by sphincter spasm.

Stimulate 3 and 4 lumbar with hot and cold sitz baths to tone pelvis. Do exercises to retain bladder.

Mild sine wave over bladder and 3 and 4 lumbar to stimulate bladder and sphincter.

DD three main remedies: *Stramonium, Hyos., Belladonna* for distention, retention, or spasm.

Epilepsy

Aconite 200c.

Indigo 6x take three every six hours.

Extosis and hemangeoma

Calc fluor 200c.

Eye wash

Parsley as a tea, dipped in cotton, very soothing to eyes.

Fever

For children, you can alternate *Kali mur* and *Ferr. phos* without any danger.

Hydrotherapy—Use heat to the feet and compresses to the chest, to get congestion out of chest.

A cool soda enema will get the temperature down rapidly (one-teaspoon of baking soda to water).

Alcohol rub. Rub the body with rubbing alcohol. Sometimes rub will make temperature go up first, then down.

Main fever remedies – *Aconite, Belladonna, Ferrum phos, Kali mur,* "work very rapidly."

Gag reflex

Simplest way to stop gag reflex. Run cold tap water on your finger. Press back part of tongue and press it down. Then pass the tube down, and there will be no gag reflex.

Gall stones

Combine tinctures of *Chionanthus, Chelidonium, Lobelia* and *Dioscoria.*
Can also be caused by a deficiency of choline and thiamin.
If bile ducts won't empty right, use coffee enemas.
Combo *China, Chionanthus, Chelidonium, Hydrastis,* each in 3x (Hyland's formula #31).
Multiple pregnancies make a woman susceptible to gall stones.
Chionanthus can be used during pregnancy, but not *Chelidonium,* or *Podophyllum. Taraxacum* is also OK.

Gall bladder

"Bucket in the well treatment."
Epson salts, and olive oil, pumped into the duodenum via a Levine Tube (weighted duodenal tube) and drain it out. Then pump it out. Suction it back up. This was treatment developed by E. .S. Larkin. Homeopath, in Bellingham who had fantastic results emptying bile. To flush out gall bladder: 2-oz olive oil, 8-oz grapefruit juice. Take at night and lie on right side until morning. Do not use in acute cases. Can be repeated 3-4 times in six months. Simple thing to do to flush gall bladder.

Beet juice or beet top diluted with carrot or dandelion greens, or with celery or any cresses, water, nasturtium.

Goiter
Spongia tosta 3x, especially if thyroid is swollen and there is a feeling of choking.

Hair growth
Capsicum, Cantharis, Bay rum. Mix together to stimulate hair.

Hay fever
1000 units of Vit C to 200 mg pantothenic acid daily.
And larger doses in multiples of this amount.

Heart problems
Convallaria is good for long term use in heart problems. Combine with *Crataegus.*
If there is arrhythmia, use *Cactus* in equal parts of *Crataegus.*
Digitalis for intermittent pulse, worse exertion with dyspnea and cyanosis. Use 3x – 6x.
Arrhythmia can be helped by potassium and magnesium aspartates. Has affinity for heart muscles.

Hernia
To prevent in children with a potential defect, use *Lycopodium* 30c once a month.

Herpes zoster
Extract of raw pig stomach. Specific for herpes zoster.
Also add 6000 units Vit E.
Extract of enzymes derived from gastric secretions, like *Protomean sulf* is one of specifics for herpes zoster.

Hot flashes
Lachesis 8x daily.

Hypothyroid

Combine tinctures of *Phytolacca, Viscum album,* and small amounts of *Nux vomica,* each in 1x to 6x tincture. Use whole plant and berries for tincture. Take daily.

Hypertension

Also *Strychnine phos* and *China arsenicosum.*

Hypertension

Veratrum veride 6x, along with *Viscum Album* and *Allium Sativa.* Equal parts *(Veratrum veride* is never used in tincture.) 10 drops of each 4 times daily.

Influenza and pneumonia

Lomatium dissectum (Leptonania).
Dr Bastyr called this remedy *Leptonania.* The appearance of a rash is a sign to lower the dose.

Intestinal spasm

(see Colic)

Keyloids

To dissolve them, use *Thiosinamine.* First thing redness leaves, contraction occurs, and it gets white. Also Vit E Some of the old doctors used injectables, for instance injecting *Thiosinamine* into scar tissue to break it up (MacKinzie), but Bastyr believed in never breaking the skin.
Also polypsia used in tincture.

Lactation

To increase milk, add iodine or carrots to the diet. Barley is another good stimulant, as is blessed thistle. Also, a teaspoon of roasted rye flower.

Lupus
Hydrocotyle asiatica 3x. "One of my good remedies for lupus."[215]

Liver remedy
Combine Senna, Wormwood, Aeolus. (Luyties combo #42.)
Berberis, China, Chel, 3x each. He used this combo for years to stimulate flow of bile. Bastyr had hundreds of cases that used this.

Liver/gall bladder tincture:
Lobelia, capsicum, dioscoria, china. 10 drops QID.
Dioscoria to relax spasm or constriction and help pass gall stones. 20 drops in hot water, repeat every few min 5-10 minutes. Then spread it out.

Lockjaw
Nux vomica 200c.

Mercury poisoning
Can use homeopathic *Mercury*. Or *Selenium*.
Also use lymphatic drainage.

Montezuma's revenge in travelers.
Use *Arsenicum* to prevent.
Concentrated extract of ginger will stop nausea within 20 minutes.

Meningitis
Belladonna. For first stage of meningitis. Hallucinations, congestion without effusions.
With effusion, think of *Apis* or *Bryonia*.
Meningitis can be brought on following a small pox vaccine.

Menses pain
Pain radiates to back during flow. *Sabina*.
Also sitz baths.

Mononucleosis

Bacillinum if is well indicated. When there is adenopathy.

Mumps

Belladonna or *Rhus tox.*

Ovarian cysts

Respond well to remedies.

Colocynth if left sided. Typical symptom, relieved by heat and pressure, like *Mag phos,* indicated because effects the belly of muscle more than the spasm. And same symptoms as *Colo.*

Make a cyst patient return after each menses. Treat for three cycles before deciding if they might need surgery, or another treatment.

Colo 30c, two times a day.

Use Magnatherm too.

Pellagra

Give Robert's Formula (AKA Bastyr's Formula).

Pleurisy

Combine tinctures of Aconite 1 dram, 7 drams, Asclepias tuberosa Lobelia, 1 dram. Take 5-10 drops hourly until perspiration is induced.

Or Bryonia for rt. sided pleurisy. If pain is relieved by lying and holding, pain with every inspiration. Knife-like shooting pains. One dose of tincture.

Proteinuria

Serum angularea 3x 6x repeated doses reduce proteinurea.

Use Samuel's technique.

Pneumonia

(See Influenza.)

Polio
Lathyrus sativa 30c.
For prevention, *Lath* 30c one dose once a week during the summer season.

Raynaud's
Use castor oil topically, after structural changes.

Sinusitis
Magnatherm, with a cooling cycle, or use Infrared, or a heat lamp. Keep near face until warm then put cold cloth over face and let it warm up.

Sea sickness
Cocculus, Tabacum
Vit B6.
Ginger will stop nausea within 20 minutes.

Shingles
(See Herpes zoster.)

Spasms pre-menses
Manipulate at insertion of cervix at third lumbar. Pressure over exit of lumbar nerve. For 1-3 minutes with your thumbs.

Sprains and bruises
Comfrey poultice.

Spleen remedy
Uvedalia – polyminia.

Strep throat
Early stages, use *Belladonna* 3x, 6x. Can be combined with *Phytolacca*.)

Spasms
Dioscoria —also lobelia.

Scars/keyloids, hemangiomas
Thiosinamine and Vit E and apply locally to remove scar.
Also acupuncture.
First thing redness leaves, contraction occurs, and it gets white.
Fluoric acid and *Calc fluor* are also good for scars. Hemangiomas as well.

Scleraderma, Calcinosis
Use castor oil topically.

Teething remedy
Cold wet socks. Cold wet cotton, cover with wool. Child will fall off and go to sleep.
Also use *Chamomilla* 3x to 30c.

Tennis elbow
Ruta 30C.
Manipulation and ultrasound.

Tic dolorous
Viscum album, 1 drop tincture a day.

Tonsils
For enlargement, use the nosodes. *Bacillinum* or *Tuberculinum,* once a month 30c or 200c, until lymphadenopathy goes down.
Also *Baryta* remedies or *Phytolacca*.

Triglyceride reduction
Guar gum and locus bean. Equal parts mixed half-and-half; take two capsules four times a day. Along with a low fat diet.

Uterine fibroids
Standard's EFF fatty acid formula. Use uterotrophin and depleting packs.
Trillium and Aletris, Senecio,
Trillium for fibroid with heavy flow, cough on exertion, lifting motion, or if after getting upright, they gush. In 3x potency, 4 pellets every hour. Or tincture. Don't give them over a 10-drop dose. Or combine Trillium tincture with Shepherd's purse and Geranium.
Amaranth – grain. Add to diet.
Diathermy and short wave or magnaterm.
Manipulate as well.

Ulcerative colitis
Aloe.
Raw pig intestines.
Brewer's yeast, and wheat germ. (Or Vit E.)

Whooping cough
Homeopathic remedies of *Drosera, Kali bi,* or *Pertussin.*
Drosera and *Pertussin* can be used as prophylactic against whooping cough.

APPENDIX

Photos

Autumn, 1972

A group of 31 mostly recent college grads waited quietly and expectantly on a cool, autumn evening in the ground floor of a small brick building in Seattle's Wallingford district

What would become the National College of Naturopathic Medicine, Class of 1976 was convening for the first time. That we were 31 was remarkable. The sophomore class above us had about 15, the junior class numbered two, and the senior class was four members. In recent memory, most students were retired from other professions, people who had always wanted to be doctors, but never got around to it.

The class of 1976 was different. We were young. We were vibrant. We were college educated. The '60s were over and left in their wake a group of young people looking for alternatives, looking for answers, looking to nature, and looking for totality. We found our way to NCNM.

Before that time, when interest in the college was diminishing, the local ND's mortgaged their homes to buy the building at 45th and Stone Way that housed the college. They taught night classes from 7 to 10 pm after a full day of seeing patients.

On this fall evening in 1973, word got out that 31 students had registered. Thirty-one were waiting to be naturopaths. Thirty-one paid tuition for the opportunity to hear them lecture.

Doctors came from miles around to see us, to speak to us, to introduce us to the gem of a science they held so dear.

Dr. Martinez, Dr. Saito, Dr. Overton, Dr. Bastyr.

They spoke to us, one at a time.

And they wept.

It was the return of the Golden Age of Naturopathy.

Dr. C.P. Bryant
photo: © Homéopathe International

Father Sebastian Kneipp
photo: NCNM Library

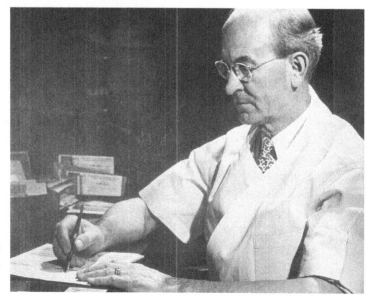

Dr. O.G. Carroll
photo: NCNM Library

Dr. Joseph Boucher
photo: NCNM Library

Dr. Arno Koegler
photo: NCNM Library

Yours for Health Truth
Herbert M. Shelton

Dr. Herbert M. Shelton
photo: NCNM Library

Dr. John Bastyr

[see Chapter 5 for more information]

"The Little Red Schoolhouse"...
the NCNM building in Seattle, Washington
1972

NCNM Class of 1976 (Dr. Bill Mitchell fourth
from right), 1973

Dr. Bastyr in a classroom at NCNM, 1973

NCNM Class of 1976 (Author Melanie Grimes
center, and Dr. Bill Mitchell on right), 1973

NCNM graduation, Class of 1972
Dr. Bastyr, second from right

Obituary

Simillimum
Journal of the Homeopathic Association of Naturopathic Physicians, Summer, 1995
(Reprinted with permission)

Memorial for Dr. Bastyr
Melanie Kornfeld Grimes
July, 1995

Dr. John Bartholomew Bastyr was born in New Prague, Minnesota in 1912. He passed away in Seattle, Washington on June 29, 1995, at the age of 83. He was a graduate of the Northwest Drugless Institute with a degree as a Sanipractic. He also had a Chiropractic Degree from the Seattle Chiropractic College. (Both schools are no longer in existence.)

At the memorial for Dr. B. attended by over 150 people, most had not met him until he was already in his 60's, the age at which most people retire.

He married Aletha LaMonde in 1937, and she passed away in 1989, well into her 90s.

Dr. Bastyr was a kind, humble man, and a great healer. He inspired a whole new generation of healers, whose lives he touched and changed.

He and his peers carried the torch of alternative medicine for many years, when there were no students, and no new practitioners. They mortgaged their homes to buy a building in which to teach naturopathic medicine to the one or two students a year who would apply. In 1972, there was a ground swell of interest in alternative healing. Over 30 college-educated youth appeared to enter the class. The doctors came from miles around to speak to us at the orientation, and they all wept.

He kept up to date on all the new, while carrying the knowledge of the old. He read voraciously, and never stopped learning, and encouraging others to study. And most of all, he healed, practicing daily until his 80's.

He delivered hundreds of babies, did underwater births decades ago, and during home births, would put newborns in shoeboxes in cooled wood stoves to keep them warm. He practiced and taught classical homeopathy to hundreds.

Dr. Bastyr was both grandfather and the father to students for the past 20 years, as there was no in between generation to be our mentors. The Naturopathic College in Seattle, Bastyr University, carries on his name.

Endnotes

1. Bastyr, John, Videotape (BU Library)
2. Ganzini, Jim, Videotape (BU Library), Bastyr Memorial 1995
3. Kirshfeld and Boyle, Nature Doctors, Buckeye Naturopathic Press, 1994
4. Bastyr, John. Videotape (NCNM Library), 1983
5. Kirshfeld and Boyle, Nature Doctors, Buckeye Naturopathic Press, 1994 pg. 303
6. Journal of Naturopathic Medicine, Volume 2, Number 1
7. From the diploma plaques at Bastyr University
8. Grimes, Melanie. Personal memoirs
9. Bastyr, John. Videotape (NCNM Library), 1983
10. Bastyr, John, Videotape (BU Library), Homeopathy. (Andrew Lange)
11. Bastyr, John, Videotape (NCNM Library), Nov 11, 1982
12. Kirshfeld and Boyle, Nature Doctors, Buckeye Naturopathic Press, 1994
13. Kirshfeld and Boyle, Nature Doctors, Buckeye Naturopathic Press, 1994
14. Bastyr, John Videotape (BU Library), Homeopathy (Andrew Lange)
15. Saine, Andre interview. "He (Bastyr) told me that when he opened his first office which was downtown Seattle, he had no desk, just two chairs, and waited for one week before the first patient came in. During that waiting time he was studying. Then a patient eventually came in. He treated him, made a bit of money and ran out to buy a table. He was never stressed with a high overhead. Slowly but surely he built up his practice without being stressed by paying bills."
16. Bastyr, John, Audiotape (NCNM Library), September 3, 1982
17. Kirshfeld and Boyle, Nature Doctors, Buckeye Naturopathic Press, 1994
18. Bastyr, John ,Videotape (NCNM Library), Lectures on Naturopathy, Tape 1, Nov 11, 1982

19. Bastyr, John Videotape (BU Library), Homeopathy (Andrew Lange)

20. Ganzini, Jim, Videotape (BU Library), Bastyr Memorial 1995

21. Grimes, Melanie. Simillimum. Fall 1995

22. Journal of Naturopathic Medicine, Volume 2, Number 1

23. Kirshfeld and Boyle, Nature Doctors, Buckeye Naturopathic Press, 1994

24. Bastyr, John, Audiotape (NCNM Library), September 3, 1982

25. Bastyr, John, Audiotape (NCNM Library), September 3, 1982

26. JNM Volume 2, Number 1

27. Grimes, Melanie, Personal memoirs

28. JNM Volume 2, Number 1

29. http://www.tcfnm.com/naturopathy.htm

30. http://www.naturalhealth.org/tradnaturo/history2.html#amnat

31. http://www.naturalhealth.org/tradnaturo/history2.html#amnat

32. http://www.naturowatch.org/hx/fishbein.html

33. http://www.ncnm.edu/a2aboutncnm/history.cfm

34. Bastyr, John, Audiotape (NCNM Library), Sept.3, 1982

35. Bastyr, John, Audiotape (NCNM Library), Sept.3, 1982

36. Bastyr, John, Audiotape (NCNM Library), Sept.3, 1982

37. Bastyr, John, Audiotape (NCNM Library), Sept.3, 1982

38. Haehl, Richard, Samuel Hahnemann,: His Life and Work. Jain Publishers, Pg. 83

39. Hahnemann, Samuel, Organon of the Medical Art, (O'Reilly ed.) Birdcage Books, 1996

40. Saine, André. Interview.1994. Vienna. Dellmour and Willinger, To Master a Discipline, We Have to Start from its Roots Upwards

41. Dorpat, Paul, Seattle Now and Then, Vol 1 and 3. Tartu Publications

42. King, Harvey, M.D. History of Homœopathy and Its Institutions in America

43. http://www.historylink.org/_output.cfm?file_id=315

44. http://seattlepi.nwsource.com/local/41047_doc02.shtml

45. King, Harvey, M.D. History of Homœopathy and Its Institutions in America

46. Bastyr, John, Audiotape (NCNM Library), Sept.3, 1982

47. Saine, André N.D, Lessons in Pure Homeopathy, From the Writings of Hahnemann's Best Student and Medicine's Most Successful Practitioner: Adolph Lippe, M.D.

48. Bastyr, John. Videotape (NCNM Library), 1983

49. Dewey, A.W. MD, Journal of the American Institute of Homeopathy May, 1921, Homeopathy in Influenza-A Chorus of Fifty in Harmony

50. Winston, Julian, Faces of Homeopathy, Great Auk Publishing, 1999, pg. 56

51. www.radar-uk.co.uk/Docs/compareG3G4.doc

52. Bastyr, John, Videotape (BU Library), Homeopathy, 1983

53. Littlefield, Charles W. MD, The Beginning and Way of Life. Rainbow Temple Association. Metropolitan Press Printers, Seattle. WA 1919

54. Littlefield, Charles W. MD, The Beginning and Way of Life, Rainbow Temple Association. Metropolitan Press Printers, Seattle. WA 1919 Pg. 433

55. Littlefield, Charles W. MD, The Beginning and Way of Life, Rainbow Temple Association. Metropolitan Press Printers, Seattle. WA 1919 Pg. 236-7

56. Bastyr, John, Videotape (NCNM Library)

57. Notation on photo at NCNM

58. Bastyr, John Audiotape (NCNM Library)

59. Bastyr, John, Videotape (NCNM Library), Nov 11, 1982

60. Bastyr, John, Audiotape (NCNM Library), Sept.3, 1982

61. Bastyr, John, Audiotape (NCNM Library), 9/3/82

62. Saine, Andre interview. One of the patients I met at John's office in 1981 was a young women who came from a kibbutz in Israel. She had been anorexic for about 8 years and had had only parenteral nutrition for the previous 5 years. Her digestive tract was completely shut down and would not digest any food that was ingested. She apparently arrived at John's skin and bone, on the brinks of death. Dr. Bastyr administered Carroll's treatment and slowly over a period of one month she was able to eat and digest anew. When I saw her was in the third month of her treatment, had regained a considerable amount of weight and was ready to return home. That evening I asked John what was this treatment with hot and cold towel he had administered to this young lady. He explained to me Dr. Carroll's treatment and encouraged me (almost pushed me) to go study with Dr. Harold Dick in Spokane. Each time I would see him afterward he would ask me, "Did you go see Dr. Dick." Some months later I went and I understood why he was so pushy about it.

63. Dewey, A.W. MD, Journal of the American Institute of Homeopathy, May 1921, Homeopathy in Influenza-A Chorus of Fifty in Harmony

64. Bastyr, John, Audiotape (NCNM Library), May 7, 1984

65. Bastyr, John, Videotape (BU Library), Homeopathy, 1983

66. Winston, Julian, Interview 2004

67. Abrams, Albert, Spondylotherapy; spinal concussion and the application of other methods to the spine in the treatment of disease, San Francisco, Philopolis Press, 1910.

68. Bastyr, John, Videotape (BU Library), Homeopathy, 1983

69. http://www.wordiq.com/definition/Albert_Abrams#The_devices

70. Vega, Fernando, Audiotape (BU Library), Bastyr Memorial, 1995

71. Moskowitz, Allen, ND. Interview, 2004, re NCNM commencement,   1976

72. Bastyr, John, Audiotape (NCNM Library), Dec 1982

73. Bastyr, John, Audiotape (NCNM Library), Endocrine system

74. Bastyr, John, Audiotape (NCNM Library), May 7, 1984

75. Bastyr, John, Audiotape (NCNM Library), May 7, 1984

76. Bastyr, John, Audiotape (NCNM Library), May 7, 1984

77. Bastyr, John, Audiotape (NCNM Library), Sept.3, 1982

78. Bastyr, John, Audio tape (NCNM Library), Endocrine system

79. Bastyr, John, Videotape (NCNM Library),Nov 11, 1982

80. Bastyr, John, Videotape (NCNM Library),1982

81. Bastyr, John, Audio tape (NCNM Library), Endocrine system

82. Bastyr, John Videotape, (BU Library),Homeopathy

83. Bastyr, John, Audio tape (NCNM Library), Endocrine system

84. Bastyr, John, Audiotape (NCNM Library), Sept.3, 1982

85. Bastyr, John ,Videotape (NCNM Library), Lectures on Naturopathy, Tape 1, Nov 11, 1982

86. Bastyr, John, Audio tape, (NCNM Library), Endocrine system

87. Bastyr, John, Audiotape (NCNM Library), Sept.3, 1982

88. Bastyr, John, Audiotape (NCNM Library),May 7, 1984

89. Bastyr, John, Audiotape (NCNM Library), Sept.3, 1982

90. Grimes, Melanie, Personal recollection

91. Bastyr. John, Videotape (NCNM Library), 1982

92. Bastyr, John, Audiotape (NCNM Library), Sept.3, 1982

93. Bastyr, John, Videotape (NCNM Library), Nov 6, 1986

94. Bastyr, John, Audiotape (NCNM Library), Endocrine system

95. Grimes, Melanie, Personal recollection

96. Bastyr, John, Audiotape (NCNM Library), Sept.3, 1982

97. Bastyr, John, Audiotape (NCNM Library), May 7, 1984

98. Bastyr, John, Audiotape (NCNM Library), Sept.3, 1982

99. Bastyr, John, Videotape (BU Library), Homeopathy. 1983

100. Bastyr, John, Audiotape (NCNM Library), Sept.3, 1982

101. Bastyr, John, Audiotape (NCNM Library), Sept.3, 1982

102. Bastyr, John, Audiotape (NCNM Library), Sept.3, 1982

103. Bastyr, John, Audiotape (NCNM Library), Sept.3, 1982

104. Bastyr, John, Audiotape (NCNM Library), Sept.3, 1982

105. Bastyr, John, Audiotape (NCNM Library), Sept.3, 1982

106. Bastyr, John, Audiotape (NCNM Library), Sept.3, 1982

107. Pizzorno, Joseph, Audiotape (BU Library), Bastyr Memorial, 1995

108. Bastyr, John, Audiotape (NCNM Library), Sept.3, 1982

109. Bastyr, John, Videotape (BU Library). Homeopathy. 1983

110. Bastyr, John, Audiotape (NCNM Library), Dec 1982

111. Bastyr, John, Videotape (BU Library), Homeopathy, 1983

112. Winston, Julian, Interview, 2004

113. Kirshfeld and Boyle, Nature Doctors, Buckeye Naturopathic Press, 1994

114. Bastyr, John, Audiotape (NCNM Library), Face and Tongue Diagnosis

115. Bastyr, John, Audiotape (NCNM Library), Jan 7, 1983

116. Bastyr, John, Videotape (BU Library), Homeopathy, 1983

117. Bastyr, John, Videotape (BU Library), Homeopathy, 1983

118. Bastyr, John, Audiotape (NCNM Library), 5/7/84

119. Bastyr, John, Videotape (BU Library), Homeopathy, 1983

120. Bastyr, John, Videotape (BU Library), Homeopathy, 1983

121. Bastyr, John, Videotape (BU Library), Homeopathy, 1983

122. Bastyr, John, Audiotape, (NCNM Library) Endocrine system, May 20, 1981

123. Bastyr, John, Videotape (BU Library), Homeopathy, 1983

124. Bastyr, John, Videotape (BU Library), Homeopathy, 1983

125. Bastyr, John Audiotape, (NCNM Library), Autoimmune disease

126. Bastyr, John, Videotape (BU Library), Homeopathy, 1983

127. Bastyr, John, Videotape (BU Library), Homeopathy, 1983

128. Bastyr, John, Videotape (BU Library), Homeopathy, 1983

129. Bastyr, John, Audiotape, (NCNM Library) Jan 7, 1983

130. Bastyr, John, Videotape (BU Library), Homeopathy, 1983

131. Bastyr, John, Videotape (BU Library), Homeopathy, 1983

132. Bastyr, John, Videotape (BU Library), Homeopathy, 1983

133. Bastyr, John, Videotape (BU Library), Homeopathy, 1983
134. Bastyr, John Audiotape, (NCNM Library)Autoimmune disease
135. Dixon, Dan, Interview, 2004
136. Bastyr, John, Audiotape, (NCNM Library), Jan 7, 1983
137. Grimes, Melanie, Personal recollection
138. Bastyr, John, Audiotape, (NCNM Library) Jan 7, 1983
139. Bastyr, John, Videotape (BU Library), Homeopathy, 1983
140. Bastyr, John, Videotape (BU Library), Homeopathy, 1983
141. Bastyr, John, Videotape (BU Library), Homeopathy, 1983
142. Bastyr, John, Videotape (BU Library), Homeopathy, 1983
143. Bastyr, John ,Videotape, (BU Library), Lectures on Naturopathy, Tape 1, Nov 11, 1982
144. Bastyr, John, Audio tape, (NCNM Library)Endocrine system, May 20, 1981
145. Bastyr, John, Audio tape, (NCNM Library)Endocrine system, May 20, 1981
146. Bastyr, John, Videotape (BU Library), Homeopathy, 1983
147. Bastyr, John ,Videotape, (NCNM Library), Dec 1982
148. Dixon, Dan, Interview, 2004
149. Bastyr, John, Videotape (BU Library), Homeopathy, 1983
150. Bastyr, John, Videotape (BU Library), Homeopathy, 1983
151. Bastyr, John, Audio tape, (NCNM Library), Endocrine system, May 20, 1981
152. Bastyr, John, Videotape (BU Library), Homeopathy, 1983
153. Bastyr, John, Videotape (BU Library), Homeopathy, 1983
154. Bastyr, John, Audio tape, (NCNM Library), Endocrine system, May 20, 1981
155. Bastyr, John, Audio tape, (NCNM Library), Endocrine system, May 20, 1981
156. Bastyr, John, Audio tape, (NCNM Library), Endocrine system, May 20, 1981
157. Bastyr, John, Audio tape, (NCNM Library), Endocrine system, May 20, 1981
158. Saine, Andre Interview. One of the patients I met in John's practice was a 98-year old lady who had an ulcerated cancer of the breast. The tumor and its ulcer were about 12 cm in diameter. I asked her how long she had it. She told me that she came to see John with the same exact size cancer of the breast when she was 65-years old. I later found out that she died of pneumonia when she was about 103.
159. Bastyr, John, Audio tape, (NCNM Library), Endocrine system, May 20, 1981
160. Bastyr, John, Videotape (BU Library), Homeopathy, 1983
161. Bastyr, John, Videotape (BU Library), Homeopathy, 1983

162. Bastyr, John, Audiotape, (NCNM Library)

163. Bastyr, John, Audiotape, (NCNM Library), Jan 7, 1983

164. Bastyr, John, Audiotape, (NCNM Library), September 3, 1982

165. Mitchell, William ND, Interview 2004

166. Bastyr, John ,Videotape, (NCNM Library), 1983

167. Bastyr, John ,Videotape, (NCNM Library), 1983

168. Bastyr, John, Audiotape, (NCNM Library), May 7, 19/84

169. Bastyr, John, Videotape(NCNM Library), Nov 11, 1982

170. Bastyr, John, Videotape (BU Library), Homeopathy, 1983

171. Bastyr, John ,Videotape (NCNM Library), 1983

172. Bastyr, John ,Videotape, (NCNM Library), 1983

173. Bastyr, John, Videotape (BU Library), Homeopathy, 1983

174. Hahnemann, Samuel, Dr., Organon of the Medical Art (O'Reilly, ed), Birdcage Books, 1996

175. Saine, Andre interview. Bastyr told me that he went to study hydrotherapy with Carroll because he had a patient with uterine fibroid who he referred to Carroll. Under Carroll's treatment the tumor was ejected per vagina, and he wanted to know how Carroll was able to achieve this. When he interned with Carroll he met a young men with tuberculosis and his name was Leo Scott who would later become a ND and continued the work of Carroll in Spokane along side of Harold Dick. All three, as well as his son Dr. Bill Carroll, that O.G. had a closet full of tumor, worms and other tissues that had been rejected by the body under hydrotherapy.

176. Bastyr, John, Videotape (NCNM Library), Nov 11, 1982

177. Bastyr, John, Audiotape (NCNM Library), May 7, 1984

178. Bastyr, John ,Videotape (BU Library), Homeopathy, 1983

179. Bastyr, John, Audiotape (NCNM Library), Sept. 3,1982

180. Mitchell, William, Plant Medicine in Practice: Using the Techniques of Bastyr, John. Churchill Livingston, 2003

181. Mitchell, William ND, Interview 2004

182. Bastyr, John, Videotape (NCNM Library), 1983

183. http://www.texas-medical.com/info/galvanicinfo.htm

184. Bastyr, John, Videotape (NCNM Library), 1983

185. Bastyr, John ,Videotape (NCNM Library), Lectures on Naturopathy, Tape 1, Nov 11, 1982

186. McKenzie, Dan, Diathermy: Medical and Surgical in Larygology, MacMillan Co, NY, 1930

187. Bastyr, John, Audiotape (NCNM Library), Sept.3, 1982

188. Bastyr, John, Videotape (NCNM Library), 1983

189. Bastyr, John, Videotape (NCNM Library), 1983

190. Bastyr, John, Videotape (NCNM Library), 1983

191. Bastyr, John, Videotape (NCNM Library), 1983

192. Bastyr, John, Audiotape (NCNM Library), Sept.3, 1982

193. Bastyr, John, Audiotape (NCNM Library), Jan 7, 1983

194. Bastyr, John, Audiotape (NCNM Library), Jan 7, 1983

195. Bastyr, John, Audiotape (NCNM Library), Gastroenterology, Jan 1983,

196. Grimes, Melanie, Personal recollection

197. Grimes, Melanie, Personal recollection

198. Bastyr, John, Videotape (NCNM Library), 1982

199. Saine, Andre interview. After my first summer of internship (1981), which I did in Montreal in my father's clinic, I had treated three women for infertility. All three became pregnant following John's approach to infertility. However, one had an ectopic pregnancy, a second one miscarried and the third one went to term. The next time I saw John in September, I told him about the two mishap cases. He said, "Of course, you have to wait 2-3 normal menses before you asked them to conceived after beginning treatment." I responded that he had never told me. It seems everything was obvious for him. I never had any more mishaps in such cases.

200. Bastyr, John, Audiotape (NCNM Library), Jan 7, 1983

201. Bastyr, John, Audiotape (NCNM Library), April 1 1983

202. Bastyr, John ,Videotape (BU Library), Homeopathy, 1983

203. Bastyr, John, Audiotape (NCNM Library), April 1 1983

204. Bastyr, John, Audiotape (NCNM Library), May 7, 1984

205. Bastyr, John, Audiotape (NCNM Library), Jan 7, 1983

206. Bastyr, John, Audiotape (NCNM Library), Jan 7, 1983

207. Bastyr, John, Audio tape (NCNM Library), Endocrine system, May 20, 1981

208. Bastyr, John, Audio tape (NCNM Library), Endocrine system, May 20, 1981

209. Bastyr, John, Audiotape (NCNM Library), 9/3/82

210. Bastyr, John, Videotape (BU Library), Homeopathy, 1983

211. Bastyr, John, Videotape (BU Library), Homeopathy, 1983

212. Bastyr, John, Videotape (NCNM Library), Nov 11, 1982
213. Bastyr, John, Videotape (BU), Homeopathy, 1983
214. Bastyr, John, Audiotape (NCNM Library), Sept 2, 1982
215. Bastyr, John, Audiotape (NCNM Library), May 7, 1984